It's another Quality Book from CGP

This book is for anyone doing AQA Modular Science at GCSE.

It contains lots of tricky questions designed
to make you sweat — because that's the only
way you'll get any better.

It's also got some daft bits in to try and make
the whole experience at least vaguely
entertaining for you.

What CGP is all about

Our sole aim here at CGP is to produce the highest quality
books — carefully written, immaculately presented and
dangerously close to being funny.

Then we work our socks off to get them out to you
— at the cheapest possible prices.

Contents

The Final Exam

Module Three — Environment

(12.1) Population and Where Species Live ..... Population and Habitat 1
(12.2) Energy and Biomass .... Food Chains and Pyramids 4
(12.3) Waste Materials .... Waste Materials and The Cycles 7
      "   " .... The Carbon Cycle 8
(12.4) Humans' Effect on the Environment .... Our Effect on the Environment 9
      "   " .... The Greenhouse Effect 10
      "   " .... Acid Rain 12

Module Four — Inheritance and Selection

(13.1) Individual Differences .... Individual Differences 13
(13.2) Breeding Plants and Animals .... Selective Breeding 15
      "   " .... Cloning 16
(13.3) Evolution   " .... Evolution 18
      "   " .... Natural Selection 19
      "   " .... Evolution and Fossils 20
(13.4) Inheritance   " .... Cystic Fibrosis 21
      "   " .... Other Genetic Diseases 22
(13.5) Controlling Fertility .... Menstrual Cycle Hormones 23

Module Seven — Patterns of Chemical Change

(16.1) Reaction Rates .... Experiments on Rates of Reaction 24
      "   " .... Collision Theory 26
      "   " .... Experiments on Rates of Reaction 27
      "   " .... Catalysts 28
      "   " .... Hazards 29
(16.2) Enzymes .... Enyzmes 30
(16.3) Energy Transfer in Reactions .... Energy Transfer in Reactions 32
(16.4) Fertiliser .... Ammonia and Fertilisers 33
(16.5) Calculations .... Relative Formula Mass 36
      "   " .... Percentage Element in a Compound 37

(AQA Syllabus reference)

Contents

The Final Exam

Module Eight — Structures and Bonding

(17.1) Bonding .... Atoms and Molecules 38
    "   " .... Atoms 39
    "   " .... Electron Arrangement 40
    "   " .... Covalent Bonding....................................... 41
    "   " .... Ions 42
    "   " .... Structures 44
(17.3) Periodic Table .... The Periodic Table 45
    "   " .... Group 0: The Noble Gases 46
    "   " .... Group I: The Alkali Metals 47
    "   " .... Group VII: The Halogens 48
(17.4) Explaining the Periodic Table ..... Electron Arrangement 49
(17.5) Compounds of Halogens .... Industrial Salt... 50
    "   " .... Uses of Halogens and Salt Products 51
(17.6) Symbols, Formulae and Equations .... Symbols, Formulae and Equations 52
    "   " .... Equations 53

Module Eleven — Forces

(20.1) Describing Motion .... Speed, Distance and Time 55
    "   " .... Speed, Velocity and Acceleration.................. 56
    "   " .... Describing Motion Graphically 57
(20.2) Speeding Up or Slowing Down ..... Speeding Up and Slowing Down 58
    "   " .... Friction 60
    "   " .... Force, Mass and Acceleration........................ 61
(20.3) Energy .... Work and Energy 62
(20.4) Orbits .... Orbits 63
(20.5) Universe and Stars .... The Universe and Stars 64
    "   " .... The Life Cycle of Stars 65

Module Twelve — Waves and Radiation

(21.1) Light and Sound Waves .... Waves: Basic Principles 66
    "   " .... Reflection and Refraction 67
    "   " .... Diffraction 68
(21.2) The Electromagnetic Spectrum ..... The Electromagnetic Spectrum 69
(21.3) Radioactive Substances .... Radioactive Substances 73
    "   " .... Effects of Radiation 74
(21.4) Radioactive Decay & Nuclear Reactors ... Atomic Structure 75
    "   " .... Radioactive Decay 76
(21.5) Ultrasound .... Sound Waves 77
    "   " .... Ultrasound 78
(21.6) Seismic Waves .... Seismic Waves... 78

Answers 79

(AQA Syllabus reference)

Contributors:

Charley Darbishire
Toby Langley
Pratheeban Nambyiah
Alison Palin
Sam Patterson
Claire Thompson
Suzanne Worthington

Based on original questions by:

Jane Cartwright
Chris Christofi
Bill Doling
Alex Kizildas
Nigel Saunders
Paddy Gannon

Proofreading by:

Hayley Kneale

Published by Coordination Group Publications Ltd.

ISBN-10: 1 84146 939 4
ISBN-13: 978 1 84146 939 3

Groovy Website: www.cgpbooks.co.uk
Printed by Elanders Hindson Ltd, Newcastle upon Tyne.
Clipart sources: CorelDRAW® and VECTOR.

12.1

Population and Place of Habitat

Plants and animals can live in very inhospitable environments,
but that's because they've adapted to their surroundings...

Q1 What do the words **predator** and **prey** mean? Give **two** examples of a predator and its prey.

Q2 Draw a table with the headings shown on the right.

In the "**factor**" column, list the things that can affect the
size of a population of organisms. In the "**examples**"
column, give an example of this factor at work.
(One row has been done for you as an example.
Think of plant examples as well as animal examples.)

Factor	Examples
Competition for water	Weeds and wheat

Q3 The Sidewinder is a snake which lives in deserts. It moves sideways across
the sand by throwing its body into a series of S-shapes, always keeping a
loop of the S-shape off the ground, with two other parts touching.

Suggest why it does this.

Q4 Many desert animals, such as the kangaroo rat, spend the day in a burrow and come out at night.

What are the **advantages** and **disadvantages** of doing this?

Q5 Desert plants are adapted to survive in their environment.

Study each of these features carefully. For each feature, decide what **condition** in the environment
the plant has adapted to, and **explain** how the adaptation helps the plant to survive in the desert.

a) The seeds of flowering desert plants can lie dormant in the soil for years
until the rain allows them to germinate, grow and flower quickly.
b) Some plants have long roots which reach deep underground.
c) Some plants have shallow roots which spread just under the surface.
d) Succulent plants store water in their leaves, stems and roots.
e) Some plants drop their leaves during a dry spell.
They usually have small leaves.
f) Some plants take in and store carbon dioxide at night.
During the day their stomata are closed.
g) Many plants have modified leaves which form thorns,
and photosynthesis occurs in the stems.

Q6 Lemmings are small rodents that live in the tundra. They have a rounded body about 12cm long.
Their fur is light brown, and they have small ears that are hidden by fur. Lemmings live in burrows.

Explain how the lemming is adapted to life in the Arctic.

Q7 Copy and complete the paragraph below. Use words from the box on the right.

In a community, the populations of predators and prey are _____ .
The population of any species is usually limited by the amount of _____
available. An _____ in the population of prey in a community means
there is more food available for its _____ . As a consequence, the
population of the predators may increase. However, an increase in the
population of the predators will mean that more _____ (prey) is
needed, and so the population of the prey will _____ .

decrease
increase
food
predators
linked *food*

12.1

<u>Population and Place of Habitat</u>

Q1   The graph below shows the average daytime temperature (line) and rainfall (bars) in the Arctic.
The temperature can fall to –80°C and the wind can blow at over 300 km/h.
It's dark all the time in winter but in the summer, the sun never sets.

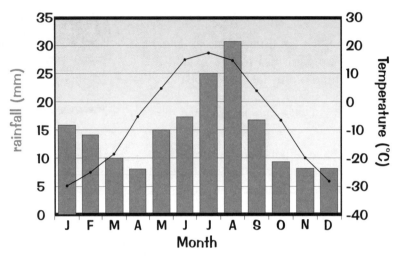

a)   Using this information, **suggest** what the environment is like in the Arctic.

b)   It's not all sea and ice in the Arctic. There is a lot of barren land too, known as the tundra.
The plants there often grow very close to the ground, and have small leaves.
Suggest a reason why the plants grow in this way.

c)   **What problems** will animals face living in the Arctic?
Suggest some adaptations that would allow animals to live successfully in the Arctic.

Q2   The camel lives in the desert — a dry, hot environment.
To help it survive, it's **adapted** to its environment in several ways.

For each of these features, say how it helps the camel survive in the desert.

a)   It has a large surface area.

b)   It can drink up to 20 gallons of water at once and store it easily.

c)   It produces little urine and even less sweat.

d)   It is a sandy colour.

e)   It has large feet.

f)   It has a hump where it stores all its fat, so there is no layer of body fat.

g)   It can tolerate big changes in its body temperature.

Q3   Just as the camel has adapted to life in the desert, the lion has adapted to
being a predator. List **three** features of the lion that make it a good predator.

Q4   List **three physical** factors which may affect an
organism's ability to live, grow and reproduce.

Population and Place of Habitat

Q1 **Copy and complete** the table to show what things plants and animals compete for.
(Hint — two of these are the same for both plants and animals.)

Plants	Animals
1)	1)
2)	2)
3)	3)

Q2 Answer the following questions about how rabbits are adapted to life as prey.

a) How does the way a rabbit moves help it to survive?

b) How does the colour of the rabbit's fur help it to avoid capture?

c) Rabbits' eyes are on either side of their heads.
How does this help them spot predators?

d) Why does the rabbit have big ears?

e) How does a rabbit's tail alert other rabbits to danger?

Q3 Complete the following paragraph about the polar bear using the words from the box. Each word can be used only once.

> white   insulation   reduces   prey
>
> thick   sheds   prevent   minimum
>
> powerful   camouflage   runner

The polar bear's surface area is kept to a _____ compared to its body weight. This _____ heat loss. It has a _____ layer of blubber for _____ . Its fur is greasy so it _____ water after swimming to _____ cooling due to evaporation. It has _____ fur for _____ and is a _____ _____ which helps it catch _____ on land.

Who you calling blubbery?

A bear adapted to 4000°C — must be a solar bear...

You may get a <u>different plant or animal</u> to the ones in this section in your exam. But apply the <u>same</u> <u>techniques</u> as you did when answering these questions and it'll be a piece of cake.

12.2

<u>Food Chains and Pyramids</u>

Food chains and pyramids. What does fast-food have to do with
the ancient Egyptians and how does that come into GCSE Science...

Q1   What does the food chain **grass** → **cow** → **man** mean in words?

Q2   **Connect** these food chains to
form a food web for these
woodland plants and animals.

tree → butterfly → robin → sparrowhawk

tree → aphid → ladybird → robin

tree → mouse → owl

grass → mouse → owl

grass → rabbit → owl

Q3   Pyramids of numbers are useful for displaying information.

a)   What **information** does a pyramid of numbers give?

b)   In the food chain, carrot → rabbit → fox, **which row**
in the table on the right represents the most likely
numbers of each organism?

c)   What do you notice about the **size** of the organism
as you look from left to right along this food chain?

d)   Which pyramid of numbers below most closely
matches the correct answer to part **b)**?

	Carrots	Rabbits	Foxes
A	1	100	4000
B	1	4000	100
C	100	1	4000
D	100	4000	1
E	4000	1	100
F	4000	100	1

e)   What do you notice about the size of the organism and the width of
its bar on the pyramid of numbers in the correct answer to part **d)**?

Q4   **Draw** pyramids of numbers for the food chains in **a)** and **b)**. Make sure you **label**
each step with the name of the organism and how many of them there are.

a)   Microscopic water plants (1 million) → water fleas (100,000) → trout (50) → kingfisher (1)

b)   Oak tree (1) → caterpillars (500) → birds (5)

c)   Ideally, the width of each bar would be drawn to scale, so that the trout bar in part **a)** would be
fifty times wider than the kingfisher bar. This is usually not possible. **Explain why**.

d)   If you have done part **b)** correctly, it will not look very pyramid-shaped.
Why can a pyramid of numbers have an unusual shape like this?

e)   **Draw** a pyramid to show the following short food chain: wheat → human. **Decide** on a suitable
width for the wheat bar. *(Hint: thousands of plants might be needed to feed one person.)*

f)   In tropical countries, a disease called schistosomiasis can be a big problem. It's caused
by a parasitic worm, about 1cm long, which lives in the blood vessels and feeds on blood.
A person might be infected by dozens of these worms. **Add** a labelled bar for the worm
to your pyramid of numbers. **Explain why** this pyramid is not pyramid-shaped.

g)   Think of another food chain that will produce a pyramid of numbers that is **not** pyramid-shaped.
Draw and **label** the pyramid, and write down the food chain alongside it.
Explain why your pyramid has its unusual shape.

Food Chains and Pyramids

Q1 Explain what is meant by the word **biomass**.
What information does a pyramid of biomass give?

Q2 One of the food chains in the North Sea is: phytoplankton → zooplankton → small fish → cod.

The biomass of each of the organisms in the food chain was estimated from samples and experiments. It was found that for every 1kg of cod, there was 100kg of phytoplankton, 80kg of zooplankton and 10kg of small fish. In each case, the masses are dry masses.

a) **Draw** a pyramid of biomass for this food chain. Draw it **to scale**, and make sure that you label each bar with the name of the organism and its biomass in kg.

b) In some pyramids of numbers and biomass, the top bar can be shown as a vertical line. **Explain** why this is sometimes necessary.

c) Between which two organisms in this food chain is the **most** mass lost? **How much** mass?

d) Between which two organisms in this food chain is the **greatest proportion** of mass lost?

e) Suggest reasons why the biomass is **less** at each level than the one before it.

f) The wet mass of a small fish averages about 1.5kg, and that of adult cod averages about 7.5kg. Assuming that both types of fish have the same proportion of water in their bodies, **how many** small fish feed one cod?

Q3 Look at these pyramids:

Explain which of the pyramids above could **represent**:

a) The pyramid of numbers for a community that relies on a large producer.
b) The pyramid of biomass for a woodland community.
c) The pyramid of numbers for a food chain that ends with parasites such as fleas.
d) The pyramid of numbers for a marine community in which the producers are tiny algae.

Q4 Fill in the blanks in the following paragraph, using the words in the box.

> The mass of living material at each stage in a food chain
> is _____ than it was at the stage below. This means
> pyramids of _____ get _____ the higher you go.
> This is not always the case with pyramids of _____.

> numbers
> less
> narrower
> biomass

It's a cod eat small fish eat zooplankton world out there...

Remember it takes <u>a lot</u> of food from the level below to keep one animal alive. <u>Pyramids of biomass</u> always get narrower the higher you go, but <u>pyramids of numbers</u> can be any shape — you have a hundred fleas on one dog, but they still weigh less than the dog. (Unless he's got them *really really* bad, that is...)

Module Three — Environment

12.2

Food Chains and Pyramids

Q1   Algae → slugs → frogs → heron ...is an example of a food chain found in a pond.

For every heron, there are 80 kg of frogs, and for every kg of frogs there are 20 kg of algae.
If there are 400 kg of frogs in the lake how many herons are there?
How much algae is there?

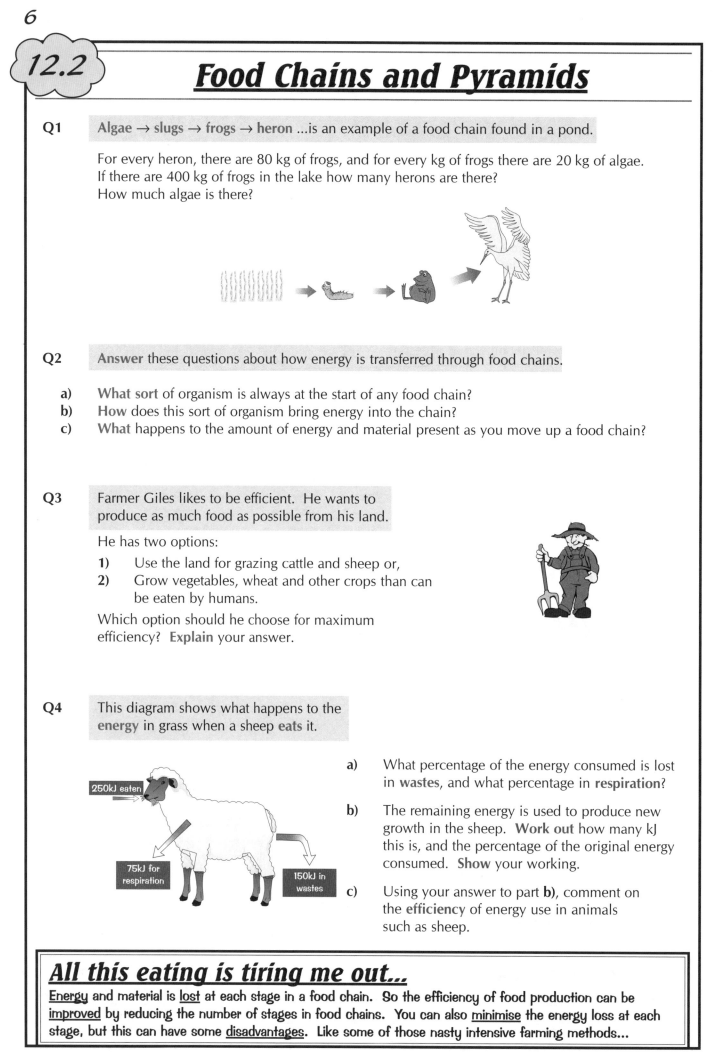

Q2   **Answer** these questions about how energy is transferred through food chains.

   a)   **What sort** of organism is always at the start of any food chain?
   b)   **How** does this sort of organism bring energy into the chain?
   c)   **What** happens to the amount of energy and material present as you move up a food chain?

Q3   Farmer Giles likes to be efficient. He wants to
produce as much food as possible from his land.

   He has two options:

   1)   Use the land for grazing cattle and sheep or,
   2)   Grow vegetables, wheat and other crops than can
           be eaten by humans.

   Which option should he choose for maximum
   efficiency? **Explain** your answer.

Q4   This diagram shows what happens to the
energy in grass when a sheep **eats** it.

250kJ eaten

75kJ for
respiration

150kJ in
wastes

   a)   What percentage of the energy consumed is lost
           in **wastes**, and what percentage in **respiration**?

   b)   The remaining energy is used to produce new
           growth in the sheep. **Work out** how many kJ
           this is, and the percentage of the original energy
           consumed. **Show** your working.

   c)   Using your answer to part **b)**, comment on
           the **efficiency** of energy use in animals
           such as sheep.

All this eating is tiring me out...

<u>Energy</u> and material is <u>lost</u> at each stage in a food chain. So the efficiency of food production can be
<u>improved</u> by reducing the number of stages in food chains. You can also <u>minimise</u> the energy loss at each
stage, but this can have some <u>disadvantages</u>. Like some of those nasty intensive farming methods...

Waste Materials and The Cycles

Q1   Material is constantly being removed from and returned to the environment.

   a)   **Why** do living things remove materials from the environment?

   b)   **How** are the materials returned to the environment?

   c)   **Why** is it important that the materials are **returned**?

Q2   Bacteria and fungi can break down solid waste materials from animals.

      They can also break down materials in dead animals and plants.
      This is known as **decomposition** or **decay**.

   a)   **What** is the benefit to the bacteria and fungi of **digesting** these materials?

   b)   **What carbon compound** will be returned to the atmosphere as a result of their activities?

   c)   **What substances** will they **release** into the soil?

   d)   **Why** are **bacteria** and **fungi** important for the recycling of carbon in the **carbon cycle**?

Q3   Microorganisms digest materials best under certain conditions.

      In each of the following statements about the conditions,
      pick the correct word from the highlighted pair.

   a)   Microorganisms digest material faster in **warm** / **cold** conditions.

   b)   They digest faster if the conditions are **dry** / **moist**.

   c)   Many microorganisms are also more active if there is **plenty of** / **not a lot of** oxygen.

Q4   Humans sometimes use microorganisms to decompose materials.

   a)   **Why** are decomposing microorganisms **added** to waste at a sewage works?

   b)   **How** do plants **benefit** from having compost put on them?

Q5   Dave's heard all about how good compost is for plants, so he's decided
      to make his own compost heap to help his amateur gardening efforts.

   a)   Dave's neighbours aren't too happy about the smell his compost
        heap gives off, so he decides to put it in his shed and keep the
        door and windows shut. **Why** will this **slow down the
        decomposition** of the material in the compost heap?

   b)   To speed things up a bit, Dave puts an electric heater in
        the shed. **Why** will this **speed up the decomposition**
        of the material in the compost heap?

Q6   For a stable community of organisms, what should processes
      that remove substances from the environment be balanced with?

Top-tips: Without microorganisms decomposing animal wastes, dead plants and animal material,
plants would have no nutrients to grow with. Then animals, like us, would have no food, and die, die, die...

12.3 The Carbon Cycle

The <u>Carbon Cycle</u> describes how carbon is removed from the environment, used by plants and animals and then returned to the environment. The <u>Spin Cycle</u> removes water from your clothes.

Q1 Green plants remove carbon from the environment.

a) What process in plants **removes** carbon dioxide from the atmosphere?

b) What process in plants **returns** some of this carbon dioxide to the atmosphere?

c) **Copy and complete** the diagram opposite using the words below. **Light** boxes are spaces for substances. **Dark** ones are spaces for processes.

| photosynthesis | carbon dioxide |
| respiration | carbon |

in the atmosphere

in green plants

d) **What three products** do plants make with the carbon from carbon dioxide?

Q2 Animals also need carbon to survive — they get it by eating green plants.

a) What happens to the carbon present in plants when they are eaten by animals?

b) What process in animals returns carbon dioxide to the atmosphere?

Q3 Explain how the carbon present in dead plant and animal material is returned to the atmosphere.

Q4 Fill in the blanks in the paragraph about the carbon cycle below, using the words in the box.

fats   microorganisms   dioxide   carbohydrates
respire   carbon   eating   proteins
respiration   green   decomposed

_____ _____ is removed from the atmosphere by _____ plants for photosynthesis. Some is returned by _____ . The carbon is used to make _____ , _____ and _____ which make up the body of the plants. Animals get carbon by _____ plants, and return some carbon dioxide to the atmosphere when they respire. Dead plant and animal material is _____ by _____ . More carbon dioxide is returned to the environment when they _____ .

Our Effect on the Environment

For a supposedly intelligent species, humans have done some pretty dumb stuff to this planet. It's no wonder none of the animals will talk to us...

Q1 With so many people in the world, we take up a lot of the room. **List four** ways that humans reduce the amount of land available for other animals and plants.

Q2 For each of the following **pollutants** produced by the human race, decide whether they affect air, land or water and put them in the appropriate column. Some pollutants may fit in more than one column.

air	land	water

sulphur dioxide   pesticides   nitrogen oxides
        sewage
carbon dioxide   herbicides   fertiliser

Q3 Mr McDoodah owns a highly successful global fast food business. There is such demand for his burgers and hot dogs that he needs **more land** to farm his cows. He decides to buy some land in the Amazon rainforest, cut down the trees and graze cattle on it.

In what **three** ways will his actions increase the amount of greenhouse gases in the atmosphere?

Q4 As you can see from the graph opposite, the world population is growing exponentially. **Answer** these questions about how this affects the environment.

a) **How** does this affect the rate of use of raw materials?

b) **What** could this mean for supplies of non-renewable energy sources such as coal, oil and gas?

c) Are the effects of human activity **larger** or **smaller** than they were 200 years ago?

d) **Explain** why the proper handling of waste has never been more important than it is now.

Q5 Most of the world's energy is produced by **burning fossil fuels** such as coal, oil and natural gas. This method of energy production has several environmental drawbacks.

a) **Name** the greenhouse gas produced by burning fossil fuels.

b) **Why** has large scale deforestation increased the amount of this gas in the atmosphere?

c) Some fossil fuels contain sulphur or nitrogen impurities. **Explain** why burning these fuels produces acid rain.

d) **Suggest** another reason why being overly reliant on fossil fuels is not a good idea. (Hint — look at Q4.)

12.4 The Greenhouse Effect

The <u>Greenhouse Effect</u> — it does exactly what it says on the tin.
If only everything in life could be that simple.

Q1 Only some of the gases in the atmosphere, called **greenhouse gases**, are good at absorbing heat energy. These include carbon dioxide and methane, which both occur naturally in the atmosphere.

a) Name a **natural source** of carbon dioxide.

b) The graph on the **right** shows the amount of carbon released from burning fossil fuels since 1850. **Describe** the graph — how has the release of carbon from fossil fuels changed? **Suggest** why this change happened.

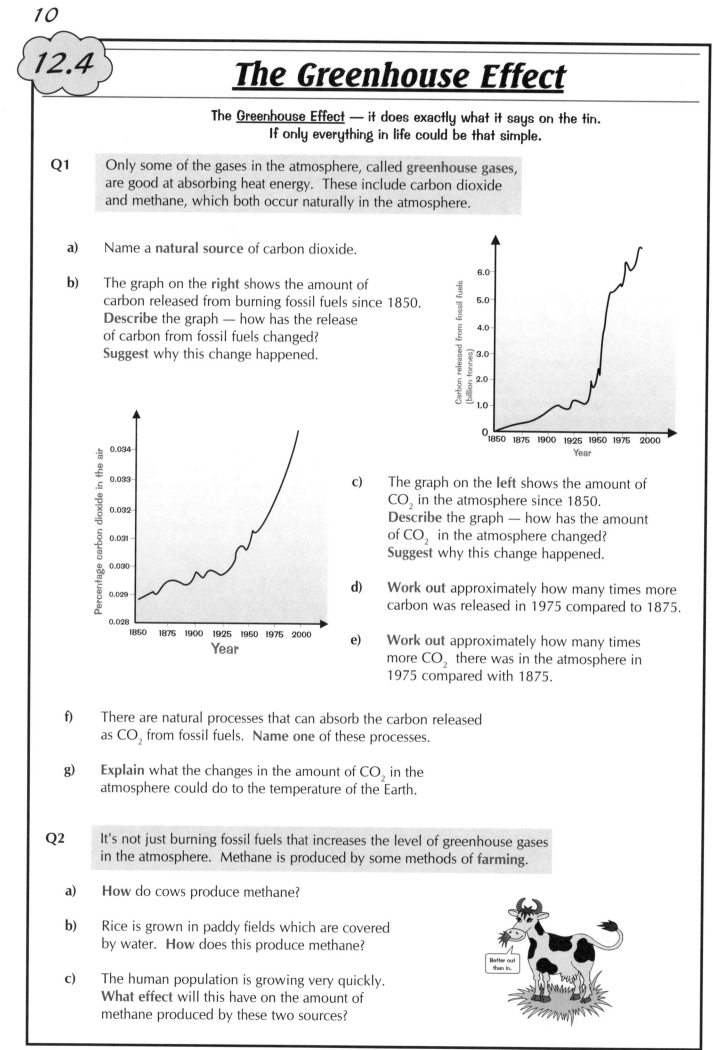

c) The graph on the **left** shows the amount of CO_2 in the atmosphere since 1850. **Describe** the graph — how has the amount of CO_2 in the atmosphere changed? **Suggest** why this change happened.

d) **Work out** approximately how many times more carbon was released in 1975 compared to 1875.

e) **Work out** approximately how many times more CO_2 there was in the atmosphere in 1975 compared with 1875.

f) There are natural processes that can absorb the carbon released as CO_2 from fossil fuels. **Name one** of these processes.

g) **Explain** what the changes in the amount of CO_2 in the atmosphere could do to the temperature of the Earth.

Q2 It's not just burning fossil fuels that increases the level of greenhouse gases in the atmosphere. Methane is produced by some methods of **farming**.

a) **How** do cows produce methane?

b) Rice is grown in paddy fields which are covered by water. **How** does this produce methane?

c) The human population is growing very quickly. **What effect** will this have on the amount of methane produced by these two sources?

Module Three — Environment

The Greenhouse Effect

Q1 Look at the graphs on the **right**. The first one shows the changes in the amount of CO_2 in the atmosphere since 1850. The second shows changes in average global temperature per year in °C since 1880.

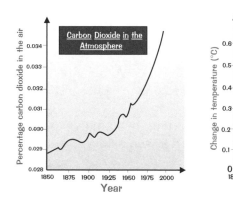

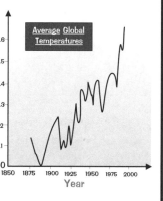

a) Describe the changes in average **temperature**.

b) Is it possible to say that the temperature changes are caused by the changes in the amount of CO_2 in the atmosphere?

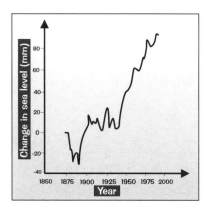

The graph on the left shows the changes in **sea level**. Compare this graph with the one showing changes in temperature.

c) **Suggest** how changes in the Earth's temperature ("Global Warming") could cause a change in sea level.

d) What do you think could happen to **low-lying** areas of the world if the amount of carbon dioxide in the atmosphere continues to rise?

Q2 The Kyoto Treaty is a pact countries sign — they agree to **limit** CO_2 emissions. President Mush has decided to abandon it.

a) The President said he wasn't convinced that carbon dioxide emissions were causing global warming. Using the graphs above, **explain** whether you agree or disagree with him.

b) He also said that limiting CO_2 emissions would be bad for **industry**. **Why** is this true?

c) **Suggest** a way to **reduce** the amount of CO_2 in the atmosphere that doesn't involve limiting the amount produced.

Q3 The Examiners' favourite phrase this year is "**sustainable development**".

a) **What** is sustainable development? (Proper definition please.)

b) **Why** is it important?

Is it getting warmer in here — or is it just me?

The examiners love this topic — they get to test your ability to make reasoned arguments. So no waffling, just state the facts and make sure you read any graphs they give you <u>very carefully</u>. Unlike Mr Mush.

12.4 *Humans' Effect on the Environment*

Acid rain is pretty bad — especially if you're a tree or
a fish. And whose fault is it? Well, ours actually...

Q1   In addition to carbon dioxide, two other harmful gases are released when
fossil fuels are burned: **sulphur dioxide** and various **nitrogen oxides**.

a)   **Write** the word equation for the formation of sulphur dioxide from sulphur and oxygen.
Use the one below for nitrogen oxides to help you.

$$\text{nitrogen} + \text{oxygen} \xrightarrow{\text{heat}} \text{nitrogen oxides}$$

When non-metal oxides dissolve in water, they produce acidic solutions.
Sulphur dioxide and nitrogen oxides are both very soluble.

b)   Using the information in the blue box above, **explain** how burning fossil fuels
produces acid rain.

c)   Power stations burn lots of fossil fuels so they are big contributors to the production of acid rain.
Suggest another source of gases that produce acid rain.

Q2   Trees are damaged by acid rain, mainly because it causes them to shed their leaves.

a)   **How** will a tree be affected if it loses its leaves?

b)   Aluminium in the soil is harmful to trees, but usually insoluble.
Acid rain dissolves aluminium — **how** will this **harm** trees?

c)   The roots of trees in acid soils can grow poorly.
How will this affect the trees?

Q3   As acid rain falls into rivers and lakes, they become increasingly acidic. Water flowing
off the land contains high levels of aluminium and mercury released by the acid rain.

a)   What will happen to the water plants in acidified lakes and rivers?

b)   Small crustaceans at the bottom of the aquatic
food chain die if the pH falls below about 6.
What will happen eventually to the other
animals in the lake if the pH falls below 6?

c)   The soluble aluminium can react with sulphuric
acid to make aluminium sulphate.
This clogs the gills of fish with sticky mucus.
Suggest the likely effect of this on the fish.

Acid rain? I must be seeing things...

There's not much to know about acid rain, so make sure you know it all really well. Remember which
gases cause it and how they are produced. Oh, and make sure you know all about its effects too.

Individual Differences

13.1

You and your mates don't look the same.
Your characteristics are *"both inherited and due to environmental factors"*.

Q1 Identical twins have the same genes, so they are genetically identical. The table shows four people, identified by the letters a, b, c and d.

Use the information in the table to identify which two people are identical twins.
Explain your answer.

Note — tongue rolling has a direct genetic cause.

Characteristic	Person			
	a	b	c	d
Have a sun tan	✔	✔		
They are male	✔	✔	✔	
They are female				✔
Can tongue roll	✔		✔	
Normal hair colour is brown	✔	✔	✔	✔
Have bleached white hair			✔	✔
Have brown eyes	✔	✔	✔	

Q2 People belong to one of these four blood groups: A, B, AB and O.

Copy and complete the paragraph below using the three words in the box.

environmental   inherited   genes

Our blood group is _____ and is not altered by _____ conditions. This means that only our _____ control which of the four blood groups we belong to.

Q3 Copy this table. Then fill in the missing information.

Organism	Number of chromosomes in a body cell	Number of pairs of chromosomes
Fruit Fly	8	
Kangaroo	12	
Rye Plant	20	
Chicken	36	
Mouse	40	
Humans	46	
Crayfish	200	

Q4 Try these questions about genes and different characteristics.

a) **Where** are chromosomes found in the body?
b) **How many pairs** of human chromosomes are there?
c) Which of the characteristics in the box below are **totally inherited**?
   *(That is, which are determined **only** by the alleles you inherit from your parents?)*

body weight, hair colour, academic ability, blood group, inherited diseases, eye colour, skin colour.

The other characteristics on the list may be affected by something else.

d) **What else** might they be affected by?

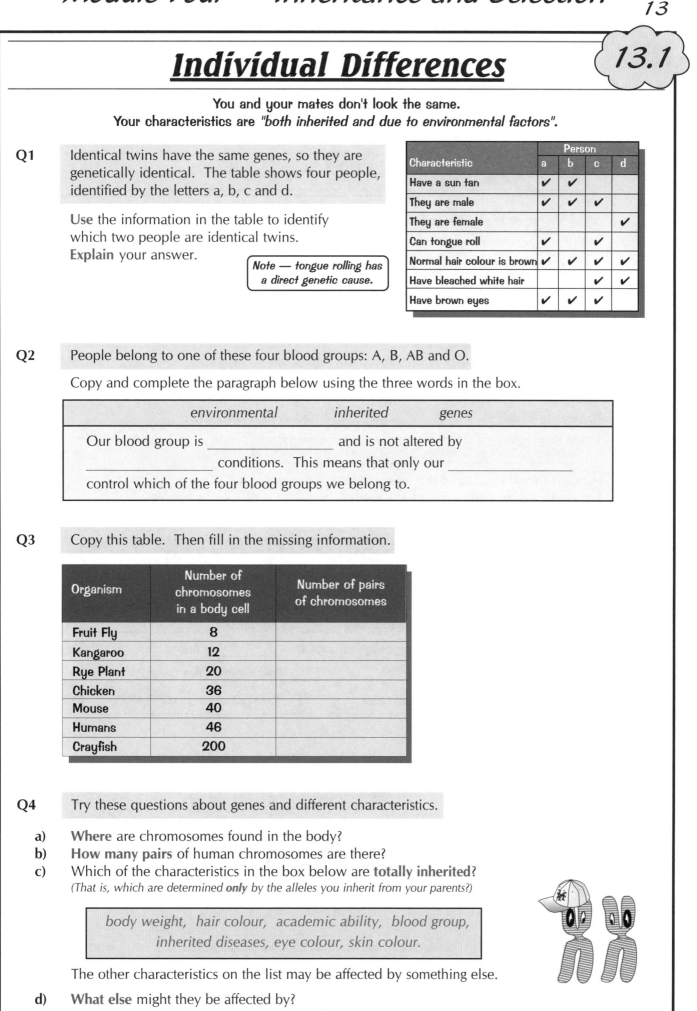

13.1 Individual Differences

Q1 Copy and complete the passage below by using each of the following words once.

> sexual   parent   without   mixing   clones   reproduction   asexually
> plant   offspring   parent   less   genes   genetic copies

Many plants can reproduce _____. This means they can produce exact _____ _____ of themselves _____ the need for another plant. The _____ of the _____ plant are _____, i.e. they have exactly the same _____ as the _____ plant. Asexual _____ produces much _____ variation in the offspring than _____ reproduction which involves the _____ of genetic information from _____ parents.

Q2 Genes, chromosomes and DNA are important things you need to know about.

a) **Draw** simple diagrams of the following items listed in the box below.

> cell   nucleus   chromosome   gene   DNA

b) Humans show lots of variation, in eye colour, hair colour etc.
Explain how **genes** give rise to this variation.

c) **Copy and complete** the following sentences using each word from the box below once.

> new   divide   growth
> multiply   replace
> divide   identical   replicating

Body cells _____ to produce _____ cells that are _____ to the original cell. The new cells continue to _____ and _____ by _____ themselves. The cells produced are used for _____ and also to _____ old cells.

Q3 Copy the table below, and put the following descriptions in the right columns.

> Only one parent is needed

> Two parents are needed

> No joining of sex cells needed

Asexual Reproduction	Sexual Reproduction

> Male and female gametes join

> Offspring are clones of parent

> Offspring are not genetically identical to parents

Selective Breeding

Manky moggies don't win cat shows — breeders look for the
best characteristics to produce the purrfect champion...

Q1   Use the following words to complete the blanks in the paragraph below:

> alleles   breed   wheat   characteristics   colours
>
> milk   people   selective   variety   varieties

Artificial selection is when _____ choose what characteristics to breed into living things. This can be used to produce new _____ and breeds of organisms. We choose the individuals which have _____ which are useful to us. We then _____ from these individuals. We choose individuals from the offspring which have the features useful to us, and breed from them. We repeat this over and over again. This is called _____ breeding. A use for this in agriculture is the production of varieties of plants and breeds of animals that produce greater yields or other desired characteristics. Examples of selective breeding in animals include the Fresian cow that produces greater _____ yields and dogs like the Basset hound that has droopy ears. Plants like _____ have been bred to grow bigger 'ears' with more grain. Also, new varieties of roses now exist with a wide range of flower _____ and shapes. However, selective breeding greatly reduces the number of _____ in a population (the gene pool) and therefore reduces _____.

Q2   People have produced new breeds of dogs to achieve either a particular look or temperament in the dog. However, some of the features we have bred in dogs are not advantageous to the dog.

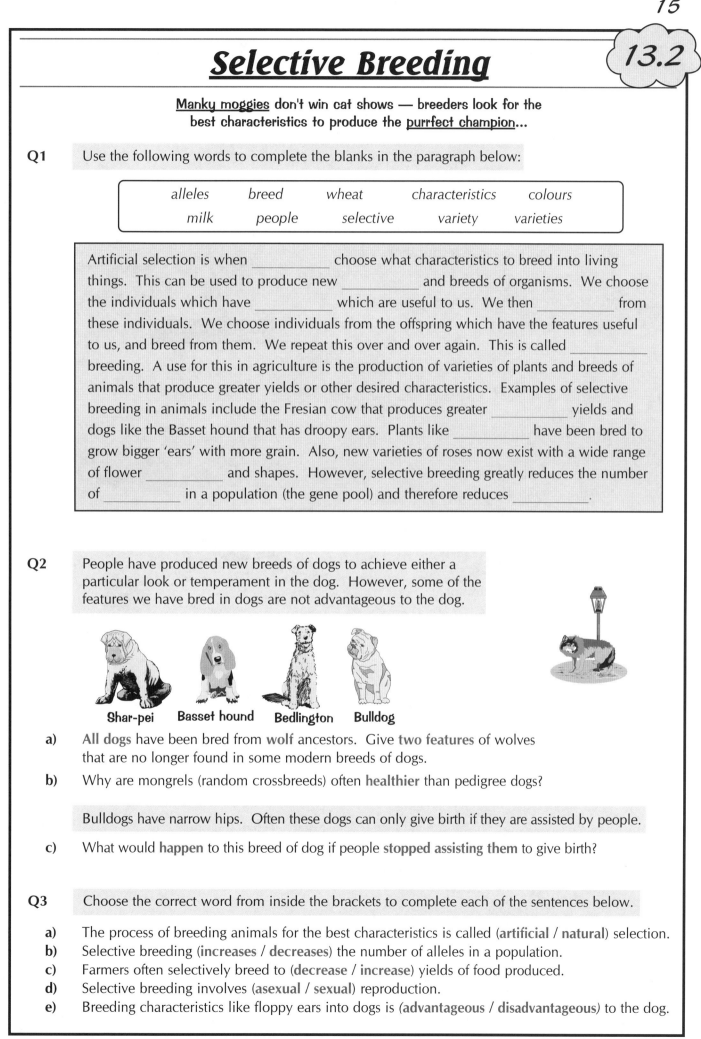

Shar-pei   Basset hound   Bedlington   Bulldog

a)   **All dogs** have been bred from **wolf** ancestors. Give **two features** of wolves that are no longer found in some modern breeds of dogs.

b)   Why are mongrels (random crossbreeds) often **healthier** than pedigree dogs?

Bulldogs have narrow hips. Often these dogs can only give birth if they are assisted by people.

c)   What would **happen** to this breed of dog if people **stopped assisting them** to give birth?

Q3   Choose the correct word from inside the brackets to complete each of the sentences below.

a)   The process of breeding animals for the best characteristics is called (**artificial / natural**) selection.
b)   Selective breeding (**increases / decreases**) the number of alleles in a population.
c)   Farmers often selectively breed to (**decrease / increase**) yields of food produced.
d)   Selective breeding involves (**asexual / sexual**) reproduction.
e)   Breeding characteristics like floppy ears into dogs is (**advantageous / disadvantageous**) to the dog.

13.2 Breeding Animals and Plants

Q1 The UK exports date-palms to Iran and oil-palms to Malaysia.
The reason we can do this is because Britain has advanced technology
in tissue culturing. The diagram shows how tissue culturing works.

a) What type of **reproduction** is this?

b) i) Why are all the plants produced **identical**?

   ii) What name is given to **identical** offspring?

c) i) What are the **advantages** of using tissue cultures?

   ii) What are the **disadvantages** of using tissue cultures?

d) What **other** technique produces identical plants?

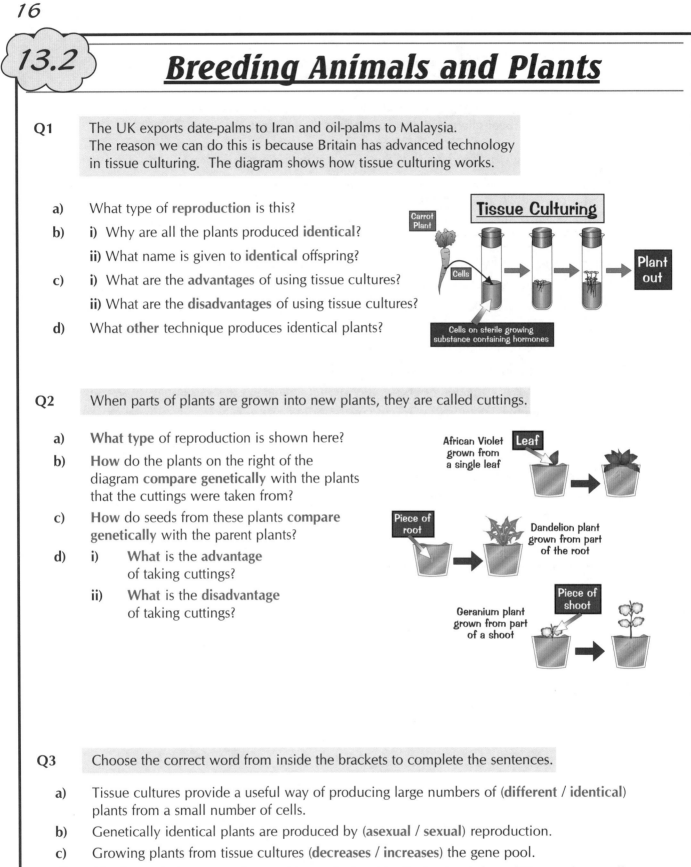

Tissue Culturing

Carrot Plant

Cells

Plant out

Cells on sterile growing substance containing hormones

Q2 When parts of plants are grown into new plants, they are called cuttings.

a) **What type** of reproduction is shown here?

b) **How** do the plants on the right of the diagram **compare genetically** with the plants that the cuttings were taken from?

c) **How** do seeds from these plants **compare genetically** with the parent plants?

d) i) What is the **advantage** of taking cuttings?

   ii) What is the **disadvantage** of taking cuttings?

African Violet grown from a single leaf — Leaf

Piece of root — Dandelion plant grown from part of the root

Geranium plant grown from part of a shoot — Piece of shoot

Q3 Choose the correct word from inside the brackets to complete the sentences.

a) Tissue cultures provide a useful way of producing large numbers of (**different** / **identical**) plants from a small number of cells.

b) Genetically identical plants are produced by (**asexual** / **sexual**) reproduction.

c) Growing plants from tissue cultures (**decreases** / **increases**) the gene pool.

d) Cloning techniques are also used in producing identical animals by splitting embryo cells (**after** / **before**) they specialise.

Top-tips: Plants — don't say much, don't listen to what you say, don't even take exams. They do some cool stuff though. Imagine if you could cut off your finger and it would grow into a whole new person. Then there'd be two yous. So you'd only have to do half the work, half the revision. Imagine...

Breeding Animals and Plants

Q1 Use the following words to complete the blanks.

| asexual | cells | cuttings | embryo | genetically | host |
| identical | mitosis | naturally | splitting | tissue | |

Clones are _____ identical organisms. These are produced in plants during _____ reproduction when _____ takes place. In plants, examples include reproduction by bulbs, stem tubers and runners, as well as _____. Using _____ cultures also results in genetically _____ offspring, plants or clones. This technique involves growing new plants from small groups of _____ from part of a plant. Cloning techniques are also used in producing identical cells in agriculture. This is done by _____ embryo cells (before they become specialised) from a developing animal _____ and then transplanting the identical embryos into a _____ mother. Clones are also produced _____ as in the case of identical twins.

Q2 The diagram shows how animal clones, like cattle, are produced in agriculture.
(That's not how that Dolly the sheep was made, by the way).

a) Why are the two offspring produced called **clones**?

b) **i)** What are the **advantages** of using this technique?
ii) What are the **disadvantages** of using this technique?

c) A farmer has a sheep with an excellent coat for making wool. The farmer wants to increase the number of sheep like this that he has.
i) Should he use **breeding** or **cloning** techniques?
ii) Give a **reason** for your answer.

Fertilized Egg
Cell Division
Embryonic Cells
Cells are split before cell specialisation
Two developing embryos transplanted into host mother to produce clones

Q3 Choose the correct word from inside the brackets to complete the sentences.

a) Genes from chromosomes within cells from humans can be removed using (**enzymes** / **alcohol**).

b) The gene removed from the (**human** / **bacteria**) cell can be inserted into a (**human** / **bacteria**) cell, where it will continue to make the same (**protein** / **carbohydrate**).

c) Large numbers of bacteria can be cultured in this way, and are used to make the large quantities of protein used in the manufacture of drugs and hormones such as human (**insulin** / **aspirin**).

Hello — haven't we met somewhere before...

Cloning. A scary sci-fi topic if ever I saw one... Remember — clones are genetically identical organisms. You need to be able to describe how plants are cloned naturally and artificially, and list the advantages and disadvantages of producing crops and livestock that are clones ... and crops and livestock that are clones.

13.3 Evolution

This section is about how plants and animals change and adapt over millions of years.
You could try looking for fossils in your garden. I'll bet you won't find any, but it'll pass the time nicely.

Q1 Use the following words to complete the blanks.

| adaptations characteristics changed environment food evolution existence |
| fittest nature organisms survival natural |

Evolution is about how living things have _____ over millions of years. Darwin proposed that organisms with the best _____ to their _____ survive and have offspring which inherit those adaptations.

Useful characteristics become more common. Less well adapted organisms die out.
All _____ over-reproduce, so individual organisms have to compete, particularly for _____. Disease and predation cause large numbers of organisms to die. This is called the struggle for _____, and leads to the survival of the _____. In other words, those individuals with the most suitable _____ are the most likely to survive.

So, _____ selects the characteristics that are going to aid _____.
This is called _____ selection. These gradual changes are the mechanism by which _____ occurs.

Q2 Place the sentences below in the right order to explain the evolution of the giraffe.

~ **mutations** resulted in some giraffes having longer necks than others.
~ **all** giraffes had **short** necks.
~ ie. **natural selection** has resulted in longer-necked offspring surviving.
~ the giraffe population had individuals whose necks **varied** in length.
~ only **long**-necked giraffes **survived** the competition for food.

In the struggle for existence...

... the suits survived

Q3 The diagram shows the earliest occurrence and abundance of fossil vertebrates.

a) What were the **first vertebrates** to evolve?

b) The dinosaurs became extinct about 60 million years ago. What **evidence** is there of this in the diagram?

c) Which were the **last vertebrates** to evolve?

d) How do fossils help us to **understand** evolution?

e) Although the diagram shows evolution as being continuous, there are many missing links in the fossil record of many animals. **How** can we **explain** these missing links?

Vertebrate Fossils

Mammals

Birds

Reptiles

Amphibia

Fish

Invertebrate ancestor

millions of years ago 100 200 300 400

Module Four — Inheritance and Selection

Natural Selection

Q1 Use the following words to fill in the blanks.

> alleles   disease   environment   favourable   offspring
> natural   die   species   survive   variation
>
> There is a wide range of _____ within particular _____ because of differences in their genes. Predation, _____ and competition (often for food) cause large numbers of individuals to _____. Individuals that survive are those that are most suited to their _____. Those individuals that survive pass on their genes (and therefore their characteristics) to their _____. This process is known as _____ selection. Natural selection can alter the frequency of particular _____ in a population. Alleles determining _____ characteristics increase in frequency. This is because alleles which enable individuals to _____ are passed on to the next generation.

Q2 The peppered moth is normally light in colour. Occasionally, a black variety appears. Insect-eating birds like the thrush prey on these moths.

a)
   i) **Why** does a **black** moth appear in a population of **light** coloured moths?
   ii) **How** is the population of these moths kept **constant**?

> In 1848, the first black variety was noticed in Manchester. By 1895, 98% of the moth population of Manchester was black. During this time, the local tree bark also became darker as a result of increasing pollution.

Peppered Moth

White and Black peppered moths on tree bark in unpolluted area

White and Black peppered moths on tree bark in polluted area

b) Why did the number of black moths **increase so dramatically** between 1848 and 1895?

c) Today, in industrialised areas, the population of dark moths is almost 100%. In Scotland and South-West England the reverse is true. **Why?**

d) **Why** is the black variety **not** a new species?

e) **What** is the name for the **process** that determines which features of a population survive?

Q3 Complete the sentences by choosing the correct words from inside the brackets.

a) The frequency of alleles which determine useful characteristics (**decreases** / **increases**) in a population.

b) Factors like disease cause a population to (**decrease** / **increase**).

c) Organisms that are the best survivors are those that are (**best suited to their environment** / **strongest**).

d) Survivors pass their genes on to their (**offspring** / **partner**).

e) Natural selection is the process by which (**evolution** / **mutation**) takes place.

f) In order for changes to occur in the characteristics of a population, (**mutation** / **predation**) must take place.

13.3 Evolution and Fossils

Q1 There are four different ways that fossils can be formed.

a) Most fossils form from the hardest parts of animals. **Fill** in the missing words in each of the sentences below then **match them** to the stages in the diagram.

i) When they die, hard parts of animals don't _____ easily. _____ collects around the dead animals and they become buried.

ii) The sediment surrounding the _____ remains also turns to rock, but the fossil stays distinct inside the rock.

iii) Over a long period of time the hard parts _____ and are replaced by _____. A rock like substance is formed in the same shape as the original hard part known as a fossil.

iv) Fossils formed in this way usually develop from hard parts of animals such as _____ , _____ and _____ . When animals die their bodies settle on the ocean floor.

In the film Jurassic Park, scientists found fully **preserved** mosquitoes that had been trapped in **amber** over **millions** of years.

b) i) What prevented them from decaying?

ii) Give two other examples of conditions that would prevent decay of dead plants and animals.

c) Sometimes the soft material of a plant or animal decays slowly and is replaced by **minerals**. Complete these sentences by choosing the correct word from the brackets.

i) This process doesn't occur very often as decay is normally very (**fast / slow**).

ii) For fossils to form in this way (known as 'petrification') a plant or animal usually has to fall into a (**swamp / swimming pool**) and be covered.

iii) The slow decay of the plant or animal is due to a lack of (**oxygen / carbon**).

Q2 In our everyday lives, we are subject to different mutation-causing influences.

a) **Why** do doctors recommend that you use suncream when sunbathing?

b) **What precautions** must a radiographer take when taking an X-ray of you and **why**?

c) **Why** is carbon tetrachloride no longer used as a cleaning agent by dry cleaners?

Q3 Earlier this century radioactive paints were used when making watches and clocks to make the numbers glow in the dark.

Why do you think many workers who made these clocks later developed throat and mouth cancer?

Survivor — but luckily no John Leslie this time...

The environment selects characteristics that make individuals survivors. Survivors pass on their genes to their children, who pass them on to theirs, and so on and so on... That's how evolution works. Mutations can lead to some pretty horrible characteristics, so many mutated genes don't stand a chance of surviving. On the odd occasion though, they can be quite handy — think of those moths...

Cystic Fibrosis

Q1   Use these words to complete the blanks.

allele	both	carriers	genetic	membranes	recessive

Cystic fibrosis is a _____ disease. One in twenty people in this country carry the recessive allele. Sufferers must have two _____ alleles. Cystic fibrosis is a disorder of cell _____.   In the lungs, the membranes produce thick sticky mucus which makes breathing more difficult and causes more infections to the lungs. Infections are treated with antibiotics. The mucus can be removed by regular physiotherapy and massage. Excess mucus is also produced in the pancreas, causing digestive problems. Sufferers have a shortened life. Since the disease is caused by a recessive _____, it must be inherited from _____ parents. Parents who have only one copy of the recessive allele are _____ of the disorder. They have no ill effects themselves.

Q2   Complete the sentences by choosing the right word from inside the brackets.

a)   Cystic fibrosis is an (**infectious** / **inherited**) disease.

b)   Cystic fibrosis is caused by a (**dominant** / **recessive**) allele.

c)   Children can inherit the cystic fibrosis disease when
(**both** / **one**) of their parents have the recessive allele.

Q3   If two carriers have children, there is a 1 in 4 chance of each child having the disease.

a)   Can children suffer from the disease if only **one** parent has a **recessive allele**?

One in twenty people carry the allele for cystic fibrosis in this country.

b)   What does "**carrying**" the allele **mean**?

Q4   Use the following words to complete the blanks:

alleles	carrier	malaria	oxygen	protected	recessive	red

Sickle cell anaemia is a disorder of _____ blood cells. It is caused by a _____ allele. Being a _____ of this disorder can be an advantage in countries where _____ is prevalent. Carriers are _____ from malaria. The disease gets its name from the shape of the red blood cells. Children who inherit two recessive _____ from their parents have red cells which are less efficient at carrying oxygen. The red blood cells also stick together in the blood capillaries. This deprives the body cells of _____.

13.4 Other Genetic Diseases

Q1 Map A shows the distribution of the sickle cell allele in Africa.
Map B shows the distribution of malaria in the same geographical region.

a) **Why** are the distributions so similar?

b) Sickle cell anaemia is a **killer** disease.

    i) What is an **advantage** for people who are **carriers** of the disease?

    ii) What is a **disadvantage** for people who are **carriers** of the disease?

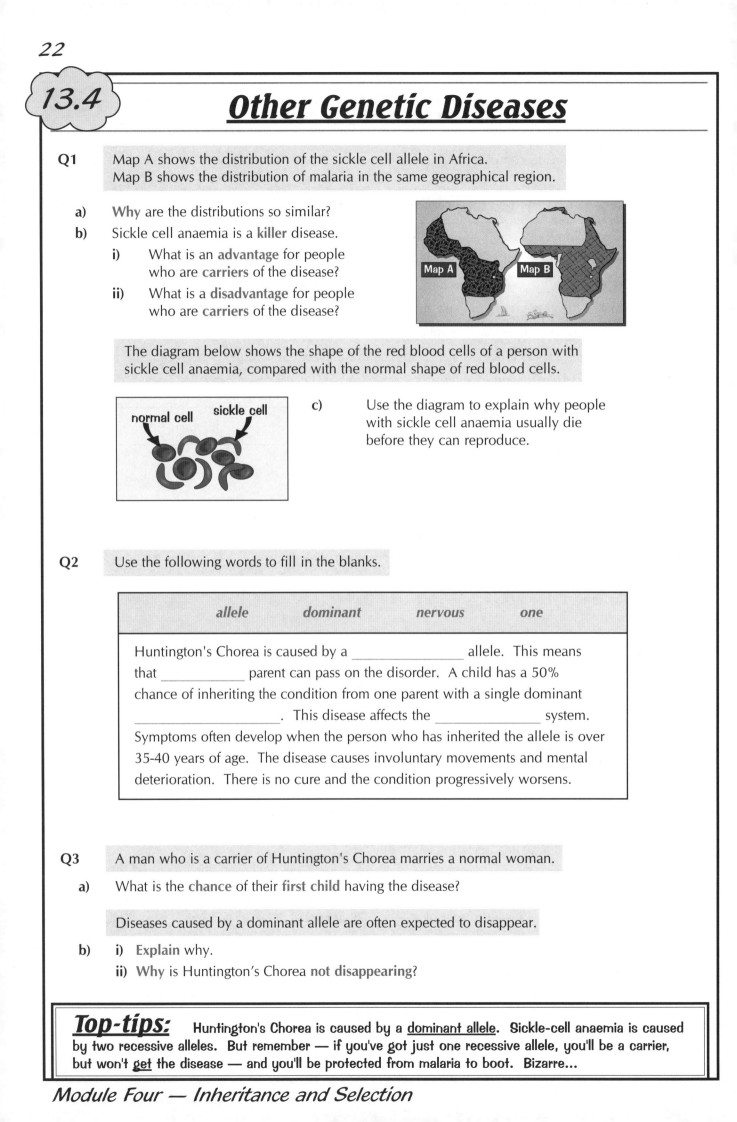

The diagram below shows the shape of the red blood cells of a person with sickle cell anaemia, compared with the normal shape of red blood cells.

normal cell   sickle cell

c) Use the diagram to explain why people with sickle cell anaemia usually die before they can reproduce.

Q2 Use the following words to fill in the blanks.

allele	dominant	nervous	one

Huntington's Chorea is caused by a _____ allele. This means that _____ parent can pass on the disorder. A child has a 50% chance of inheriting the condition from one parent with a single dominant _____. This disease affects the _____ system. Symptoms often develop when the person who has inherited the allele is over 35-40 years of age. The disease causes involuntary movements and mental deterioration. There is no cure and the condition progressively worsens.

Q3 A man who is a carrier of Huntington's Chorea marries a normal woman.

a) What is the **chance** of their **first child** having the disease?

Diseases caused by a dominant allele are often expected to disappear.

b) **i)** **Explain** why.

    ii) **Why** is Huntington's Chorea **not disappearing**?

Top-tips: Huntington's Chorea is caused by a <u>dominant allele</u>. Sickle-cell anaemia is caused by two recessive alleles. But remember — if you've got just one recessive allele, you'll be a carrier, but won't <u>get</u> the disease — and you'll be protected from malaria to boot. Bizarre...

Controlling Fertility

Q1   In total, four **hormones** control menstruation.

a)   **Name the two places** where they are produced.

b)   **Copy the diagram** on the right and indicate where the two hormone-producing locations are in the body.

Q2   The diagram below shows the different stages of the **menstrual cycle** and the beginning of a **pregnancy**. Study it, then answer the following questions.

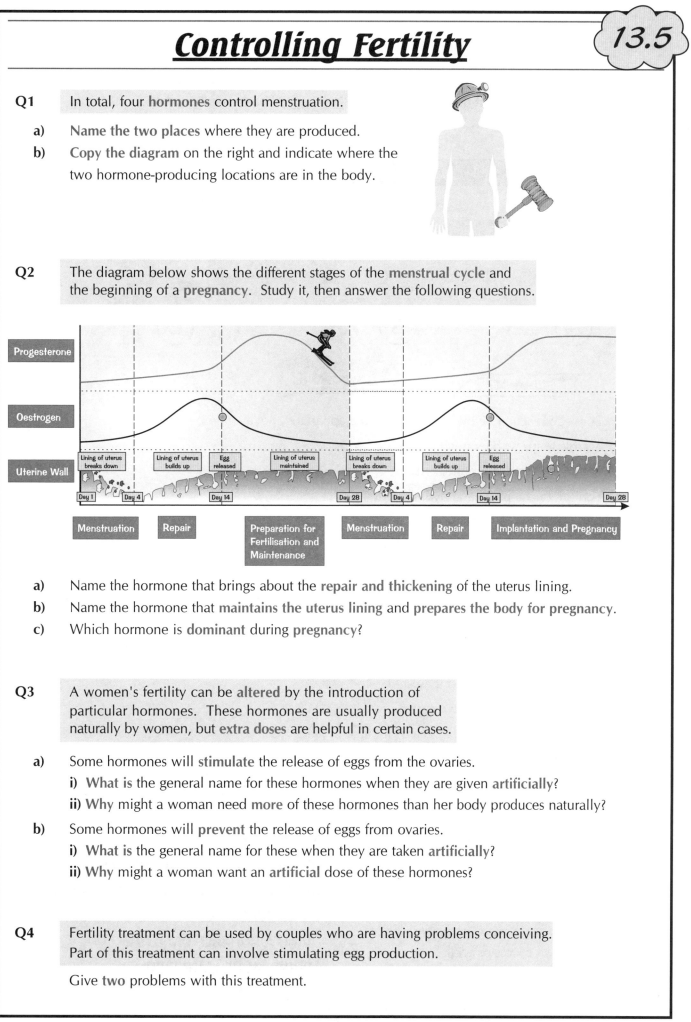

a)   Name the hormone that brings about the **repair and thickening** of the uterus lining.

b)   Name the hormone that **maintains the uterus lining** and **prepares the body for pregnancy**.

c)   Which hormone is **dominant** during **pregnancy**?

Q3   A women's fertility can be **altered** by the introduction of particular hormones. These hormones are usually produced naturally by women, but **extra doses** are helpful in certain cases.

a)   Some hormones will **stimulate** the release of eggs from the ovaries.

i) **What is** the general name for these hormones when they are given **artificially**?

ii) **Why** might a woman need **more** of these hormones than her body produces naturally?

b)   Some hormones will **prevent** the release of eggs from ovaries.

i) **What is** the general name for these when they are taken **artificially**?

ii) **Why** might a woman want an **artificial** dose of these hormones?

Q4   Fertility treatment can be used by couples who are having problems conceiving. Part of this treatment can involve stimulating egg production.

Give **two** problems with this treatment.

16.1 Experiments on Rates of Reaction

Reactions don't just happen, like a cat and dog in a small box, eventually things will go off.
What you need to know is <u>how long</u> different reactions take.

Q1 Place these chemical reactions **in order** of their speed, starting with the fastest reaction:

| Frying an egg | Striking a match | A car rusting | Concrete setting | Digesting food |

Q2 The rate of a chemical reaction can be measured either by watching for the
disappearance of reactant or the **appearance of product**. Look at the apparatus below.

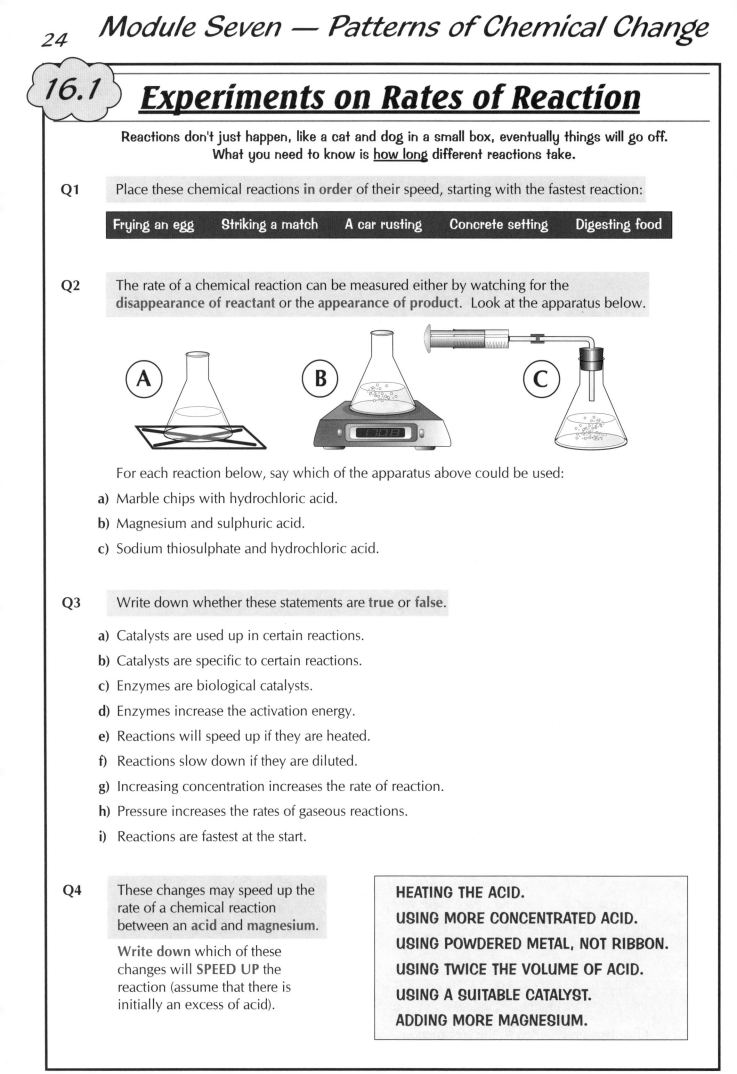

For each reaction below, say which of the apparatus above could be used:

a) Marble chips with hydrochloric acid.

b) Magnesium and sulphuric acid.

c) Sodium thiosulphate and hydrochloric acid.

Q3 Write down whether these statements are **true** or **false**.

a) Catalysts are used up in certain reactions.

b) Catalysts are specific to certain reactions.

c) Enzymes are biological catalysts.

d) Enzymes increase the activation energy.

e) Reactions will speed up if they are heated.

f) Reactions slow down if they are diluted.

g) Increasing concentration increases the rate of reaction.

h) Pressure increases the rates of gaseous reactions.

i) Reactions are fastest at the start.

Q4 These changes may speed up the
rate of a chemical reaction
between an **acid** and **magnesium**.

Write down which of these
changes will **SPEED UP** the
reaction (assume that there is
initially an excess of acid).

HEATING THE ACID.

USING MORE CONCENTRATED ACID.

USING POWDERED METAL, NOT RIBBON.

USING TWICE THE VOLUME OF ACID.

USING A SUITABLE CATALYST.

ADDING MORE MAGNESIUM.

Experiments on Rates of Reaction 16.1

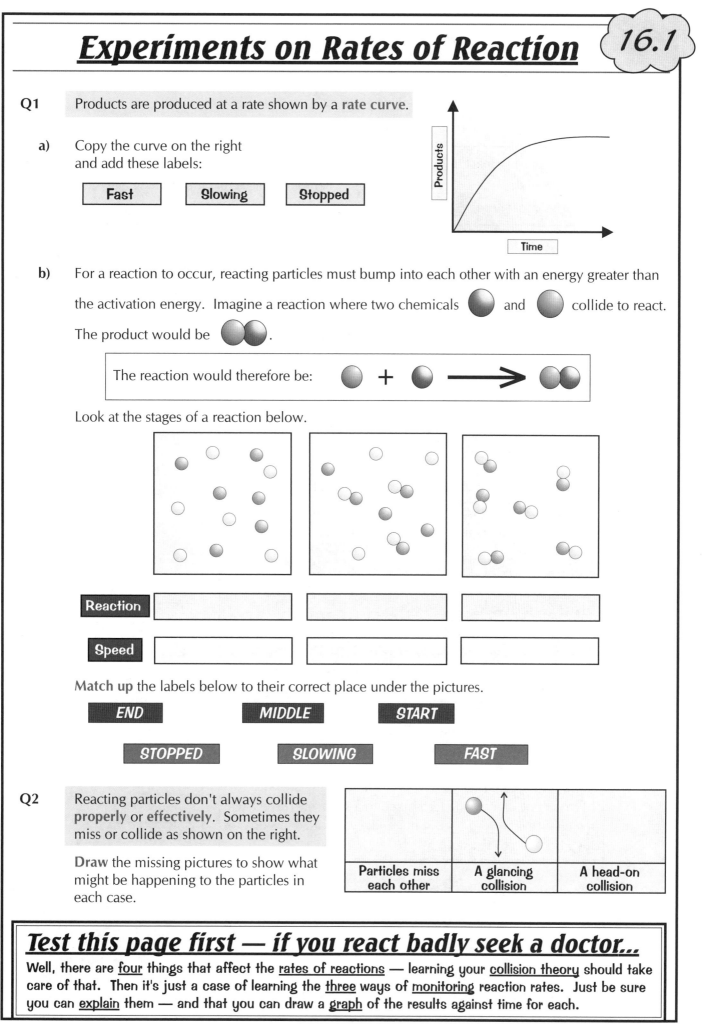

Q1 Products are produced at a rate shown by a **rate curve**.

a) Copy the curve on the right and add these labels:

| Fast | Slowing | Stopped |

b) For a reaction to occur, reacting particles must bump into each other with an energy greater than the activation energy. Imagine a reaction where two chemicals ⬤ and ⬤ collide to react.

The product would be ⬤⬤.

The reaction would therefore be: ⬤ + ⬤ ⟶ ⬤⬤

Look at the stages of a reaction below.

Reaction [ ] [ ] [ ]

Speed [ ] [ ] [ ]

Match up the labels below to their correct place under the pictures.

| END | MIDDLE | START |

| STOPPED | SLOWING | FAST |

Q2 Reacting particles don't always collide **properly** or **effectively**. Sometimes they miss or collide as shown on the right.

Draw the missing pictures to show what might be happening to the particles in each case.

| Particles miss each other | A glancing collision | A head-on collision |

Test this page first — if you react badly seek a doctor...

Well, there are <u>four</u> things that affect the <u>rates of reactions</u> — learning your <u>collision theory</u> should take care of that. Then it's just a case of learning the <u>three</u> ways of <u>monitoring</u> reaction rates. Just be sure you can <u>explain</u> them — and that you can draw a <u>graph</u> of the results against time for each.

26

16.1 Collision Theory

Q1   Fill in the blanks below using each word once.

energy   collide   energy   activation   catalyst   concentration

Particles can only react if they _____ with enough _____ for the reaction to take place.
This is called the _____ _____. There are four factors that can change the rate of a
reaction: temperature; _____; surface area and the use of a suitable _____.

Q2   Fill in the blanks in the text and complete the diagrams below using each word once.

moderate   faster   energy   surface area   faster   fast   slow   particles   faster
faster   more often   collision   successful   slow   fast
faster   low concentration   catalyst present   high concentration   large surface area

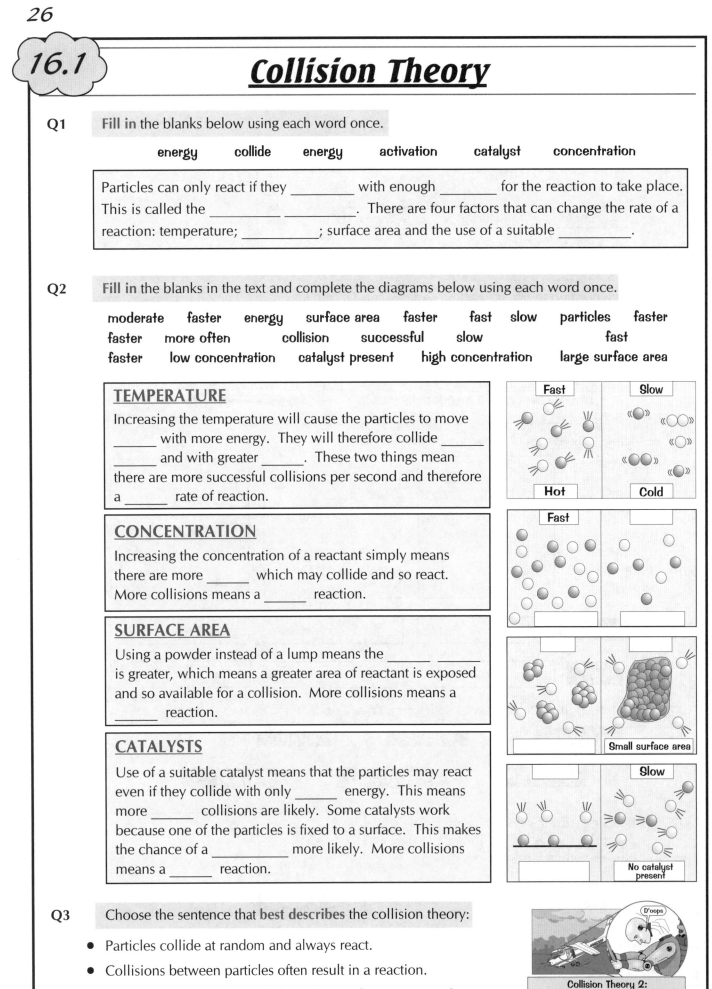

TEMPERATURE

Increasing the temperature will cause the particles to move
_____ with more energy. They will therefore collide _____
_____ and with greater _____. These two things mean
there are more successful collisions per second and therefore
a _____ rate of reaction.

CONCENTRATION

Increasing the concentration of a reactant simply means
there are more _____ which may collide and so react.
More collisions means a _____ reaction.

SURFACE AREA

Using a powder instead of a lump means the _____ _____
is greater, which means a greater area of reactant is exposed
and so available for a collision. More collisions means a
_____ reaction.

CATALYSTS

Use of a suitable catalyst means that the particles may react
even if they collide with only _____ energy. This means
more _____ collisions are likely. Some catalysts work
because one of the particles is fixed to a surface. This makes
the chance of a _____ more likely. More collisions
means a _____ reaction.

Q3   Choose the sentence that **best describes** the collision theory:

- Particles collide at random and always react.

- Collisions between particles often result in a reaction.

- Reacting particles must collide with enough energy in order to react.

- Collisions between molecules are sometimes needed before a reaction occurs.

Module Seven — Patterns of Chemical Change

Experiments on Rates of Reaction 16.1

Q1 The reaction between sodium thiosulphate and hydrochloric acid produces a yellow precipitate of solid sulphur. This makes the solution cloudy and stops us seeing clearly through it. The cross below the flask in the diagram will slowly disappear as more precipitate is produced.

In an experiment to investigate rates of reaction, the time taken for the cross to disappear was measured.

50cm³ of sodium thiosulphate solution was used and 10cm³ of hydrochloric acid was added.

The experiment was repeated at different temperatures.

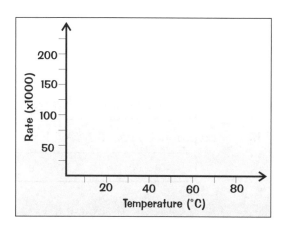

Temperature (°C)	20	30	40	50	60	70
Time taken (s)	163	87	43	23	11	5

a) **Copy the graph** on the right and use the results above to plot a line showing the relationship between temperature and time taken.

b) **Use the graph** to draw a simple conclusion about the effect of temperature on the time taken for the reaction to finish.

c) The rate of a reaction may be found by dividing 1 by the time taken (1/t). Copy the table above and add a row with the reaction rate at each temperature.

d) **Plot a graph** of rate against temperature. (If the actual numbers for the rate value are too small to plot, use 'Rate×1000' on the vertical axis).

e) **From the graph**, work out how temperature affects the **rate** of a chemical reaction.

f) Use your knowledge of the collision theory to **explain** your conclusion.

Q2 The same reaction can be used to investigate the effect of **concentration** on the rate of a reaction. When changing the concentration, it is important to keep the total volume used exactly the same.

Volume of sodium thiosulphate (cm³)	50	40	30	20	10
Volume of water (cm³)	0				
Time taken (s)	80	101	137	162	191
Rate (1/t)					

a) **Complete** the table above, adding the volume of water and calculating the rate of the reaction (to four decimal places).

b) **Copy** the axes on the right. Then, using data from the table, show how the volume of sodium thiosulphate used affects the time taken and rate of the reaction.

c) Use these graphs to draw a **simple conclusion** about the effect of concentration on the reaction rate.

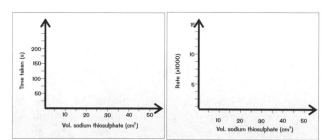

16.1 Catalysts

Q1   Write down whether these characteristics of catalysts **a)** to **g)** are **advantages** or **disadvantages**.

a)   Catalysts increase the speed of a reaction.

b)   Catalysts can be expensive.

c)   Catalysts can be used again and again.

d)   Catalysts work without being used up.

e)   In some reactions catalysts may need to be cleaned.

f)   Catalysts can be used to allow reactions to occur at much lower temperatures.

g)   Catalysts can be used in continuous production processes.

Q2   Different catalysts are used in different reactions.
Name the catalysts used in the two reactions below:

a)   The Haber Process:

> Nitrogen   +   Hydrogen   ⇌   Ammonia

b)   The production of Nitric Acid:

> Ammonia   +   Oxygen   →   Nitrogen monoxide + Water

Often catalysts are used in the form of a powder, pellets or a gauze.

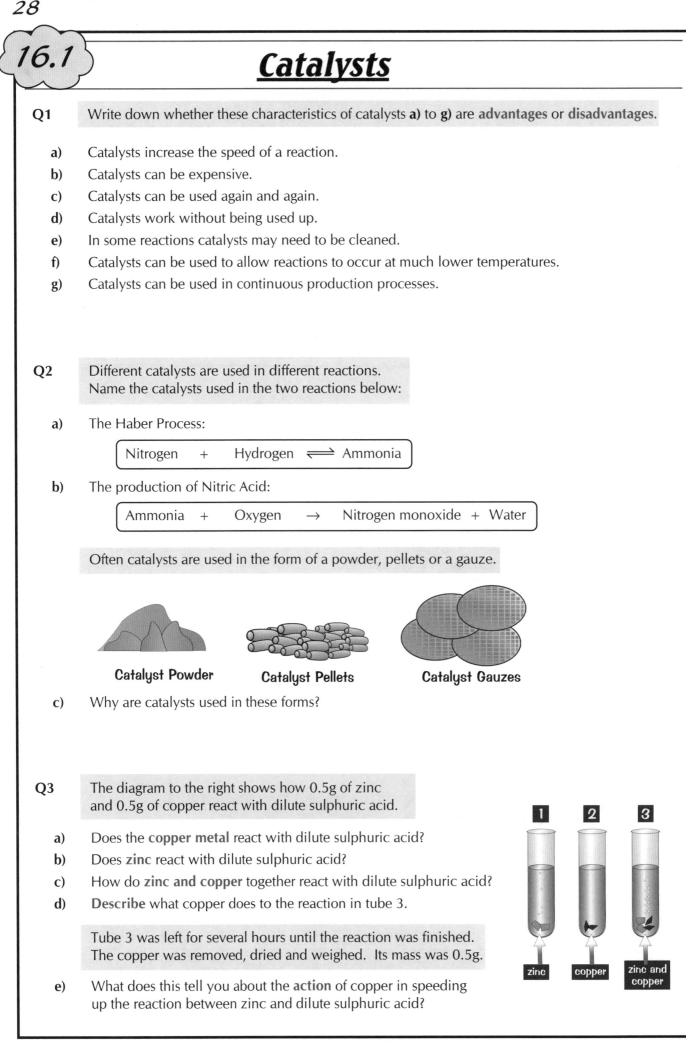

Catalyst Powder   **Catalyst Pellets**   **Catalyst Gauzes**

c)   Why are catalysts used in these forms?

Q3   The diagram to the right shows how 0.5g of zinc
and 0.5g of copper react with dilute sulphuric acid.

a)   Does the **copper metal** react with dilute sulphuric acid?

b)   Does **zinc** react with dilute sulphuric acid?

c)   How do **zinc and copper** together react with dilute sulphuric acid?

d)   **Describe** what copper does to the reaction in tube 3.

Tube 3 was left for several hours until the reaction was finished.
The copper was removed, dried and weighed. Its mass was 0.5g.

e)   What does this tell you about the **action** of copper in speeding
up the reaction between zinc and dilute sulphuric acid?

zinc   copper   zinc and copper

Hazards

Q1 Link up the hazchem (hazardous chemical) symbols with their description. Give an **example** of each.

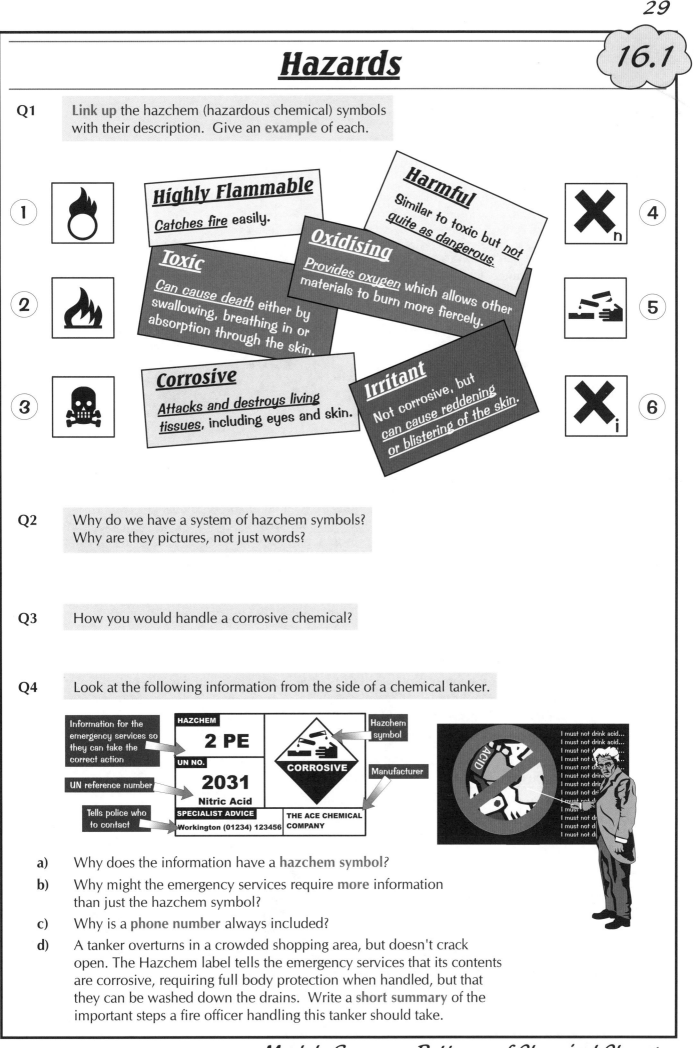

1

Highly Flammable
Catches fire easily.

Harmful
Similar to toxic but _not_ quite as dangerous.

4

Oxidising
Provides _oxygen_ which allows other materials to burn more fiercely.

2

Toxic
Can cause death either by swallowing, breathing in or absorption through the skin.

5

3

Corrosive
Attacks and _destroys living tissues_, including eyes and skin.

Irritant
Not corrosive, but can cause _reddening or blistering of the skin._

6

Q2 Why do we have a system of hazchem symbols?
Why are they pictures, not just words?

Q3 How you would handle a corrosive chemical?

Q4 Look at the following information from the side of a chemical tanker.

Information for the emergency services so they can take the correct action

HAZCHEM
2 PE

UN reference number

UN NO.
2031
Nitric Acid

Tells police who to contact

SPECIALIST ADVICE
Workington (01234) 123456

Hazchem symbol

CORROSIVE

Manufacturer

THE ACE CHEMICAL COMPANY

I must not drink acid...
I must not drink acid...
I must not d...
I must not d...
I must not dri...
I must not drink...
I must not dri...
I must not dri...
I must...
I must not dr...
I must not dr...
I must not dj...

a) Why does the information have a **hazchem symbol**?

b) Why might the emergency services require **more** information than just the hazchem symbol?

c) Why is a **phone number** always included?

d) A tanker overturns in a crowded shopping area, but doesn't crack open. The Hazchem label tells the emergency services that its contents are corrosive, requiring full body protection when handled, but that they can be washed down the drains. Write a **short summary** of the important steps a fire officer handling this tanker should take.

16.2 <u>Enzymes</u>

Q1   Cheese goes mouldy after a while.

a)   What causes cheese and other foods to go off?

b)   Why does cheese stay fresh for longer if kept in a fridge?

c)   **Explain** why meat or vegetables in a freezer can stay fresh for months.

phew!

Q2   Suggest what part enzymes might play in the
following pictures. Use the headings to help you.

1. Laundry

2. Slimming Food

Trim The
FAT

Fructose   Glucose

3. Babyfood

Q3   Professor Slashenburn, a megalomaniac, has decided to set up a factory in the middle of the
Sahara (he lives in Cumbria, and would quite enjoy a bit of sun for a change). Rumours
quickly spread that he is up to no good. Some claim that he's shipping in exotic bacteria for
his experiments. In addition, his factory soon begins spewing out large quantities of smoke.
The local superhero, Sultanaman, suspects the fumes may contain carbon dioxide.

a)   Sultanaman finds four chemicals he thinks he can use to detect Carbon Dioxide.
They are shown in the box below. Which one is the right choice?

i) Copper Sulphate Soln.   **ii)** Limewater   **iii)** Hydrochloric Acid   **iv)** Ammonia

b)   The test shows that the fumes are indeed CO_2. The locals don't like the idea of the use of nasty
CO_2 producing enzymes and challenge Prof. Slashenburn to explain the use of such enzymes.
Which of the arguments below could he use?

  i)   "Enzymes are creatures with feelings and enjoy a hard day's work."

 ii)   "Enzymes allow reactions to occur at normal temperatures and pressures
reducing the need for expensive and demanding equipment."

iii)   "Enzymes produce vast quantities of carbon dioxide which creates a nice
warm environment for us all."

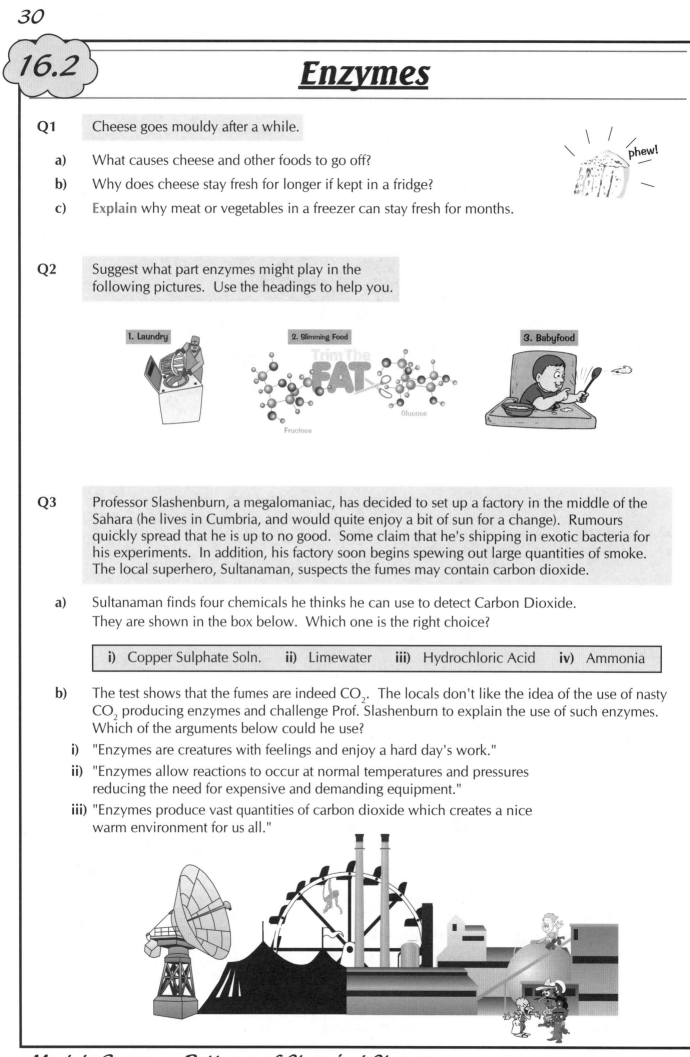

Enzymes

Q1 The enzymes in yeast help to produce energy from sugar. They can do this by breaking down glucose into carbon dioxide and ethanol.

a) Fill in the gaps to **balance** the equation below.

$$C_6H \square O \square \rightarrow 2C \square H \square OH + \square CO_2$$

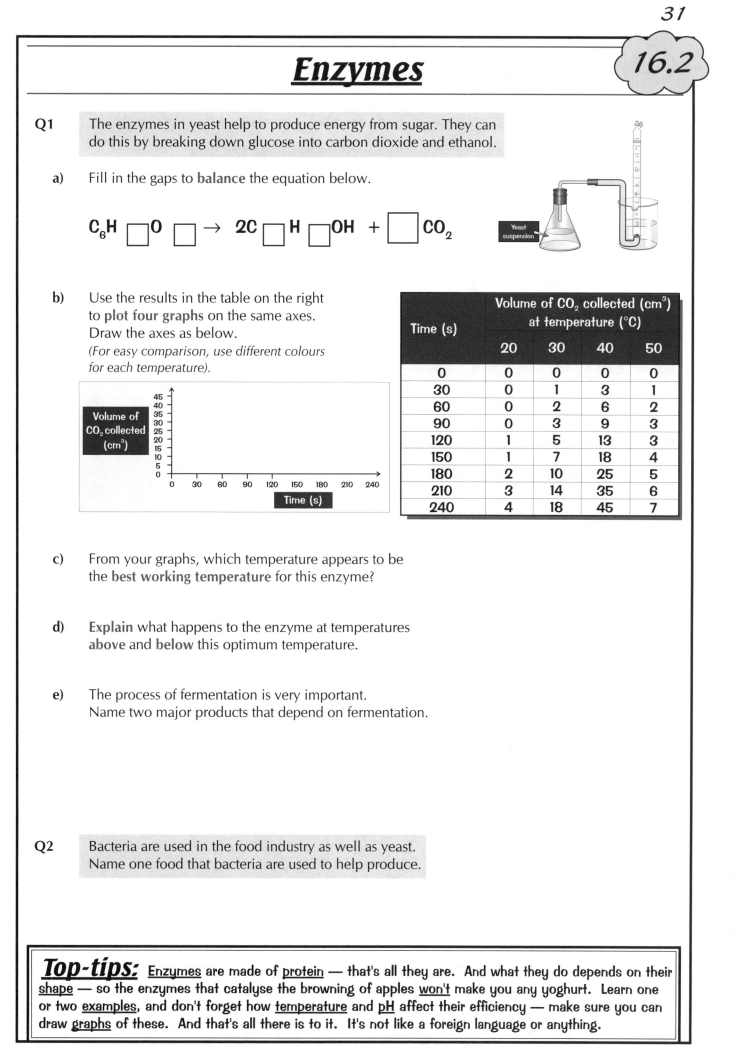

Yeast suspension

b) Use the results in the table on the right to **plot four graphs** on the same axes. Draw the axes as below.
   (For easy comparison, use different colours for each temperature).

Volume of CO₂ collected (cm³)

45
40
35
30
25
20
15
10
5
0

0   30   60   90   120   150   180   210   240

Time (s)

Time (s)	Volume of CO_2 collected (cm³) at temperature (°C)			
	20	30	40	50
0	0	0	0	0
30	0	1	3	1
60	0	2	6	2
90	0	3	9	3
120	1	5	13	3
150	1	7	18	4
180	2	10	25	5
210	3	14	35	6
240	4	18	45	7

c) From your graphs, which temperature appears to be the **best working temperature** for this enzyme?

d) **Explain** what happens to the enzyme at temperatures **above** and **below** this optimum temperature.

e) The process of fermentation is very important. Name two major products that depend on fermentation.

Q2 Bacteria are used in the food industry as well as yeast. Name one food that bacteria are used to help produce.

Top-tips: Enzymes are made of _protein_ — that's all they are. And what they do depends on their _shape_ — so the enzymes that catalyse the browning of apples _won't_ make you any yoghurt. Learn one or two _examples_, and don't forget how _temperature_ and _pH_ affect their efficiency — make sure you can draw _graphs_ of these. And that's all there is to it. It's not like a foreign language or anything.

16.3 Energy Transfer in Reactions

Q1   Fill in the blanks in the following passage (the words can be used more than once):

energy	exothermic	endothermic	cold
taken in		hot	given out

a) A reaction that gives out _____ is called an _____ reaction. A reaction that takes in _____ is called an _____ reaction.

b) _____ reactions can feel _____ as energy is _____ _____. _____ reactions can feel _____ as energy is _____ _____.

Brrrr....!

Phew!

Q2   **Classify these reactions** or changes as **exothermic** or **endothermic**:

a)   Burning a fuel.

b)   Neutralising an acid.

c)   Thermal decomposition of calcium carbonate.

d)   Rapid oxidation of iron.

e)   Rapid dissolving of ammonium nitrate.

Q3   Look at the two diagrams opposite.

a)   Write **word equations** for both the reactions in the diagrams.

b)   What does the **symbol** "⇌" mean?

c)   Use this symbol to rewrite your answer to part **a)** as a **single** equation.

Conc. HCl on cotton wool   Conc. NH₃ on cotton wool

NH₄Cl

Red litmus paper going blue - showing ammonia to be present

Ammonium chloride

Heat

Q4   Copper sulphate can be either blue crystals or a white powder.

Blue Crystals ⇌ White Powder

a) How can you change the **blue crystals** to a **white powder**?

b) How can you **reverse** the process?

c) Write a **word equation** to describe this change.

Top Tips: This sort of thing's difficult at first — but once it's clicked, you'll remember it. Don't forget that in a <u>reversible</u> reaction the <u>products</u> of the reaction can react again to form the original <u>reactants</u>. If a <u>reversible</u> reaction is <u>endothermic</u> in one direction it's <u>exothermic</u> in the other.

Ammonia and Fertilisers

Q1   Why is the Haber Process **so important**?

Q2   The two gases used to make ammonia in the Haber Process are hydrogen and nitrogen.

   a)   **Where** does the nitrogen come from?
   b)   **Where** does the hydrogen come from?

Q3   Look at the diagram opposite.

   a)   How do the iron catalysts on
          large trays affect the reaction?

   b)   What is the **function** of the condenser?

   c)   Why is the reaction at a temperature of
          450°C and a pressure of **200 atm**?

   d)   How would a **very low temperature**
          affect the rate of this reaction?

   e) | Nitrogen + Hydrogen ⇌ Ammonia. |

          What does the symbol " ⇌ " mean?

   f)   What happens to the **unused** reactants?

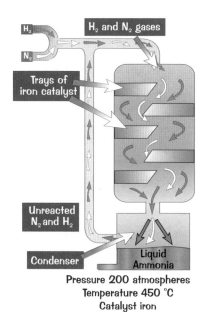

Pressure 200 atmospheres
Temperature 450 °C
Catalyst iron

Q4   In the production of ammonia, the yield increases as the pressure is increased.
         However, at a given pressure, the lower the temperature, the greater the yield.

   a)   Which of the two yield curves shown on
          the **graph** indicates the yield at 450°C
          and which 350°C?

   b)   Why is a **lower temperature** not used
          in ammonia production?

   c)   What other conditions are used in the process
          to ensure **rapid** production of ammonia?

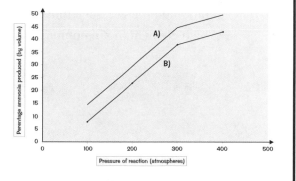

Top Tips: You need to know the factors that improve the <u>rate of reaction</u> and the <u>yield</u>. Don't
forget, yield and rate of reaction are favoured by different factors, so the <u>industrial conditions</u> are a
<u>compromise</u>. The stuff on this page can be <u>boring</u>, but you do need to know them.

16.4 — Ammonia and Fertilisers

Q1 The reaction that produces ammonia is shown below:

Nitrogen + Hydrogen $\rightleftharpoons$ Ammonia

$$N_2 + 3H_2 \rightleftharpoons 2NH_3$$

a) This reaction is **exothermic** (in the forward direction). What does this mean?

b) The yield at a lower temperature is higher, yet the temperature chosen for this process is high. **Explain** why such a high temperature is chosen.

Q2 Ammonia is made into fertilisers in three main stages.
Firstly, the ammonia needs to be converted into nitric acid.

Step 1 $\qquad 4NH_{3(g)} + 5O_{2(g)} \rightarrow 4NO_{(g)} + 6H_2O_{(l)}$

a) Name the **products** made in the reaction.

b) Ammonia reacts with oxygen as shown in this equation above.
What conditions are needed?

Step 2 $\qquad 4NO_{(g)} + 3O_{2\,(g)} + 2H_2O_{(g)} \rightarrow 4HNO_{3(aq)}$

c) Name the **product** made in this reaction.

Step 3 | Nitric acid then needs to be converted into ammonium nitrate.

d) What **type** of reaction is this?

e) **Write** a word equation for this reaction.

f) Ammonium nitrate is a fertiliser.
Which **element** in ammonium nitrate is particularly useful for plants?

Q3 The **Haber Process** works using nitrogen taken from air in the atmosphere.
What proportion of the Earth's atmosphere is nitrogen?

Ammonia and Fertilisers

Q1   **Complete** the following passage about the production of fertilisers, using the words given.

> neutralised   ammonium nitrate   oxidised   cooled
>
> fertilisers   nitrogen monoxide   oxygen   nitric acid
>
> water   nitric acid   ammonia

Ammonia is _____ to form nitric acid. In the first stage in the

production of _____, _____ is formed and

needs to be _____ before it goes into the next stage.

The nitrogen monoxide reacts with _____ and _____

to form _____.

The _____ is then _____ with

_____ to form _____ fertiliser.

Q2   Ammonia compounds make good inorganic fertilisers.

a)   Name an **inorganic fertiliser** and state how they differ from **organic fertilisers**.

b)   Which **element** within the ammonia compound is particularly useful to crops?

Q3   If the Haber Process ceased and ammonium compounds were not made, what effect would this have on:

a)   The production of **fertilisers**?

b)   The production of **crops**?

Fertilise your mind — with this page...

Fertilisers are needed to provide important <u>nutrients</u> for <u>plants</u>, particularly food crops. Don't forget the ways that nitrate fertilisers can <u>pollute</u> the water, and what farmers can do to <u>reduce</u> this problem.

Relative Formula Mass

EXAMPLE: Find the **relative atomic mass** of zinc.
(Which is basically the same as asking...."Find the Mass of One Mole of Zinc".)

> **Look on the Periodic Table (at the front of the book)
> for the relative atomic mass of zinc, which is 65.**
>
> (add a "g" for grams if you're asked for a mole)
>
> <u>Answer</u> = <u>65g</u>

Q1   Find the **relative atomic mass** of...

a)   Calcium (Ca)   **b)**   Sodium (Na)   **c)**   Iron (Fe)
d)   Chlorine (Cl)   **e)**   Aluminium (Al)   **f)**   Mercury (Hg)

EXAMPLE: Find the **relative formula mass** of zinc oxide.
(Which is basically the same as asking...."Find the Mass of One Mole of Zinc oxide")

> **Simply add up the relative atomic masses of zinc and oxygen
> (65 + 16).** (Then put a "g" for grams if it asked for a mole)
>
> **Zinc oxide has a formula ZnO. Which contains:**   (1 x Zn) + (1 x O)
>   = (1 x 65) + (1 x 16)
>   =   65   +   16
>   =   <u>81g</u>

Q2   Find the **relative formula mass** of...

a)   Hydrogen molecules (H_2)   **b)** Oxygen molecules (O_2)   **c)** Chlorine molecules (Cl_2)
d)   Bromine molecules (Br_2)   **e)** Nitrogen molecules (N_2)   **f)** Fluorine molecules (F_2)

Q3   Calculate the **relative formula mass** of the following compounds:

a)   Copper oxide (CuO)   **b)** Hydrogen chloride (HCl)   **c)** Sodium chloride (NaCl)
d)   Carbon monoxide (CO)   **e)** Sodium bromide (NaBr)   **f)** Lithium iodide (LiI)

Q4   Calculate the **relative formula mass** of these more complex compounds:

a)   Carbon dioxide (CO_2)   **b)** Water (H_2O)   **c)** Ethene (C_2H_4)
d)   Barium sulphate ($BaSO_4$)   **e)** Lead iodide (PbI_2)   **f)** Aluminium oxide (Al_2O_3)

Percentage Element in a Compound 16.5

Calculations = loads of easy marks once you've got them sussed. Read on to find out how...

Remember this formula:

$$\text{\% Mass of an element in a compound} = \frac{A_r \times \text{No. of atoms (of that element)}}{M_r \text{ (of whole compound)}}$$

Here's an example worked out for you:

Find the % mass of sodium in Na_2SO_4.

REMEMBER: A_r = Relative Atomic Mass; M_r = Relative Molecular Mass

A_r of sodium = 23, A_r of sulphur = 32, A_r of oxygen = 16

So A_r of Na_2SO_4 = $(2 \times 23) + 32 + (4 \times 16)$ = 142

So % mass of sodium = $\dfrac{A_r \times n}{M_r} \times 100$ = $\dfrac{23 \times 2}{142} \times 100$ = <u>32.4%</u>

Q1 Using the Periodic Table at the front of this book, find the percentage mass of:

a) Carbon in CO_2
b) Carbon in CO
c) Potassium in KCl
d) Sodium in NaF
e) Copper in CuO
f) Sulphur in SO_2
g) Oxygen in SO_2

h) Sulphur in SO_3
i) Oxygen in SO_3
j) Hydrogen in H_2O
k) Nitrogen in NH_3
l) Sodium in $NaOH$
m) Water in $CuSO_4.5H_2O$
n) Aluminium in Al_2O_3

o) Copper in $CuCO_3$
p) Copper in $CuSO_4$
q) Potassium in KNO_3
r) Phosphorus in $(NH_4)_3PO_4$
s) Nitrogen in NH_4NO_3
t) Nitrogen in $(NH_4)_2SO_4$

Q2 Which of the compounds below has the greatest percentage of carbon? Show how you **calculated** your answer.

CH_4 , C_6H_6 or C_2H_5OH

Q3 Which of the compounds below has the greater **percentage** of aluminium?

Al_2O_3 or Na_3AlF_6

Q4 Which of these iron ores has the most iron in it by **percentage** mass...

...Siderite ($FeCO_3$), Haematite (Fe_2O_3), Magnetite (Fe_3O_4) or Iron pyrite (FeS_2)?

Top-tips: The <u>relative mass</u> of each <u>element</u> in a compound is needed to calculate the relative mass of that compound. You need to be able to calculate the exact <u>percentage</u> of each element in a compound using the <u>relative mass</u> of each one. So remember the <u>formula</u> at the top of this page.

17.1   **Atoms and Molecules**

Atoms may be dead small, but everything is made from them — so they're pretty important...

Q1   From these diagrams, choose the letter of the pictures that best describe:

a)   A **pure** element.

b)   A **pure** compound.

c)   A **mixture** of elements.

d)   A **mixture** of compounds.

e)   An example of molecules made from just **two elements**.

f)   An example of molecules made from **three elements**.

g)   Which example could be **water**?

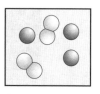

A   B   C

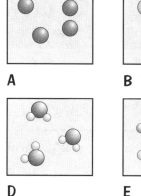

D   E   F

Q2   Who re-introduced the idea of the atom around 200 years ago?

Q3   Methane can be represented in the following ways:

Molecular formula: CH_4

Structural formula:
```
      H
      |
  H — C — H
      |
      H
```

Molecular model: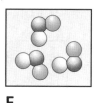

Complete the table for the following named substances:

Name	Molecular formula	Structural formula	Molecular model
Water		O H H	
Ammonia	NH_3		
Ethane		H H H–C—C–H H H	
Carbon dioxide			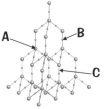

Q4   Use the following words to label A, B and C on this molecular model of silicon dioxide, SiO_2 (sand).

silicon   oxygen   covalent bond

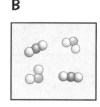

A ←   → B

← C

Let's stick together guys...

Atoms join up to make molecules. The "join" is a chemical bond and the arrangement of atoms is shown in a molecular model. You can show a molecule as a molecular formula or a structural formula or build a three dimensional model with little coloured balls and sticks, which is far more fun.

Atoms

Q1   Answer these questions on atoms:

a)   What is an **atom**?
b)   **How many** different types of subatomic particles make up an atom?
c)   What are their **names**?
d)   What is a **nucleus**?
e)   What is an **electron shell**?

Q2   **Fill in the labels** A, B and C on the diagram opposite.

Q3   **Copy and complete** the table below:

Particle	Mass	Charge	Where it is found
Proton	1		
Electron		-1	
Neutron			In the nucleus

A_____

B_____

C_____

Q4   More details on atoms:

a)   **Where** is most of the mass in an atom concentrated?
b)   What is in between the **nucleus** and the **electrons**?

Q5   Nuclear reactions affect the nucleus. What do **chemical reactions** affect?

Q6   All atoms are neutral. If an atom has **seven** electrons then **how many protons** does it have?

Q7   Answer these questions on the atomic number and mass number of an element:

a)   What does the **atomic number** tell us?
b)   What does the **mass number** tell us?
c)   What do the letters **A** and **Z** in the diagram stand for? What is A–Z?
d)   How many **protons** are there in an atom of lithium?
e)   How many **electrons** are there in an atom of lithium?
f)   How many **neutrons** are there in an atom of lithium?
g)   Which **number** (*mass or atomic*) determines what element an atom is?

A ⟶ 7

Li

Z ⟶ 3

Q8   **Calculate** the number of protons, electrons and neutrons in the following:

a)   Carbon ($^{12}_{6}\text{C}$)   b) Potassium ($^{39}_{19}\text{K}$)   c) Hydrogen ($^{1}_{1}\text{H}$).

Q9   Some questions on isotopes:

a)   What are **isotopes**?
b)   Uranium 235 and uranium 238 are isotopes.
     Are they chemically different? **Explain** why.

Time for some learnin'... Some tricky new terms here — that's science for you. Make sure you know the difference between atomic number and mass number. Come the exam it'll be easy marks...

Module Eight — Structures and Bonding

17.1 Electron Arrangement

Electron arrangement is easy. In fact it's very easy. All you need to remember is
that the first shell can hold two and all others can hold eight. Then just fill 'em up...

Q1 Copy and complete these diagrams using crosses to show the **full
electronic arrangement** — and write it down in numbers too.
The first three have been done for you.

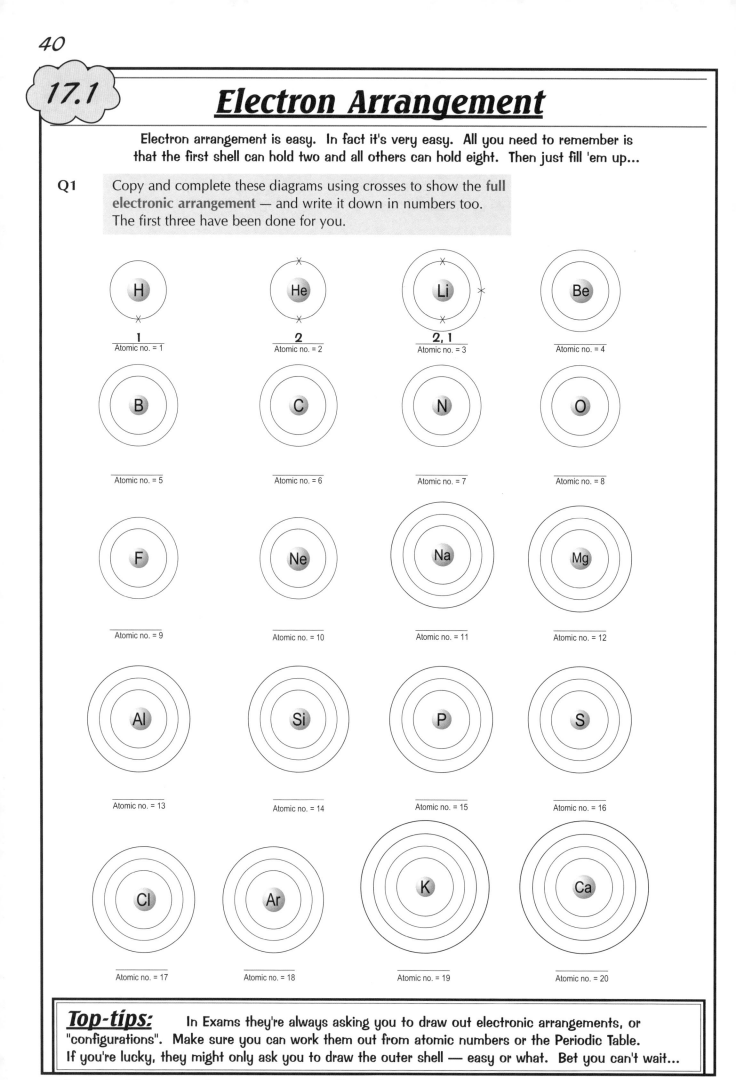

Top-tips: In Exams they're always asking you to draw out electronic arrangements, or
"configurations". Make sure you can work them out from atomic numbers or the Periodic Table.
If you're lucky, they might only ask you to draw the outer shell — easy or what. Bet you can't wait...

Module Eight — Structures and Bonding

Covalent Bonding

Atoms join up to make <u>molecules</u>. They do this by forming chemical <u>bonds</u>. A chemical bond always involves <u>electrons</u>. A covalent bond is one where atoms <u>share</u> one or more pairs of electrons. This means that both the atoms can effectively have a <u>full outer shell</u>.

A full shell is a more stable arrangement of electrons, like in noble gases. Noble gases are <u>inert</u> and <u>very</u> <u>stable</u>. Don't forget, atoms undergo chemical reactions to attain a <u>full shell</u>, which makes them <u>more</u> <u>stable</u> — and that's why atoms react to make compounds. Got all that — then you can answer these:

Q1   What is a **molecule**?

Q2   What is the name for the **joining** of two atoms?

Q3   What do **two** atoms **covalently bonded** share?

Q4   **Copy the diagram** on the right. Then **draw two crosses** on these circles to show the electrons in a single covalent bond:

Q5   Why do atoms **share** electrons?

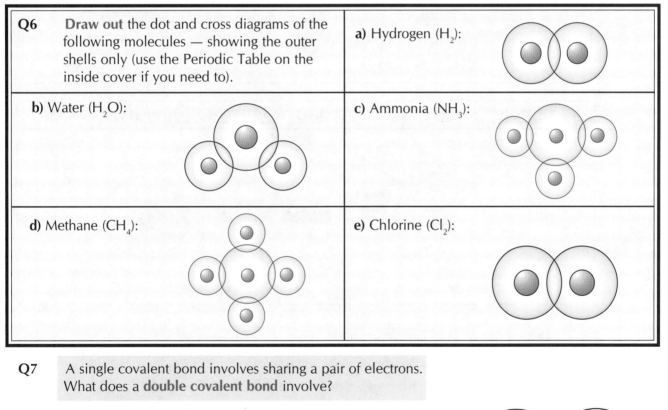

Q6   **Draw out** the dot and cross diagrams of the following molecules — showing the outer shells only (use the Periodic Table on the inside cover if you need to).

a) Hydrogen (H_2):

b) Water (H_2O):

c) Ammonia (NH_3):

d) Methane (CH_4):

e) Chlorine (Cl_2):

Q7   A single covalent bond involves sharing a pair of electrons. What does a **double covalent bond** involve?

Q8   An oxygen atom can attain a full shell by forming a double bond with another oxygen atom.

Using dots and crosses show a double bond on the molecule to the right and label it. Then fill in the other electrons.

Oh hydrogen, you make me feel so complete...

Just remember atoms "like" to have a full outer shell, so some atoms will <u>share electrons</u> so that they "feel" like they've got a full outer shell. It's all so romantic.

17.1 Ions

Q1 Answer these questions about ions:

a) What is an **ion**?
b) Give **two** examples of ions made from single atoms.
c) Give **two** examples of ions made from several atoms.
d) **Complete** this paragraph using the words provided:

-ve protons negatively charged neutral positively charged

Atoms are electrically _____ because they have equal numbers of _____ (+ve) and electrons (____). If electrons are taken away from a metal atom or hydrogen, it becomes _____ _____ because it has less electrons than protons. If electrons are added to a non-metal atom, it becomes _____ _____ because it then has more electrons than protons.

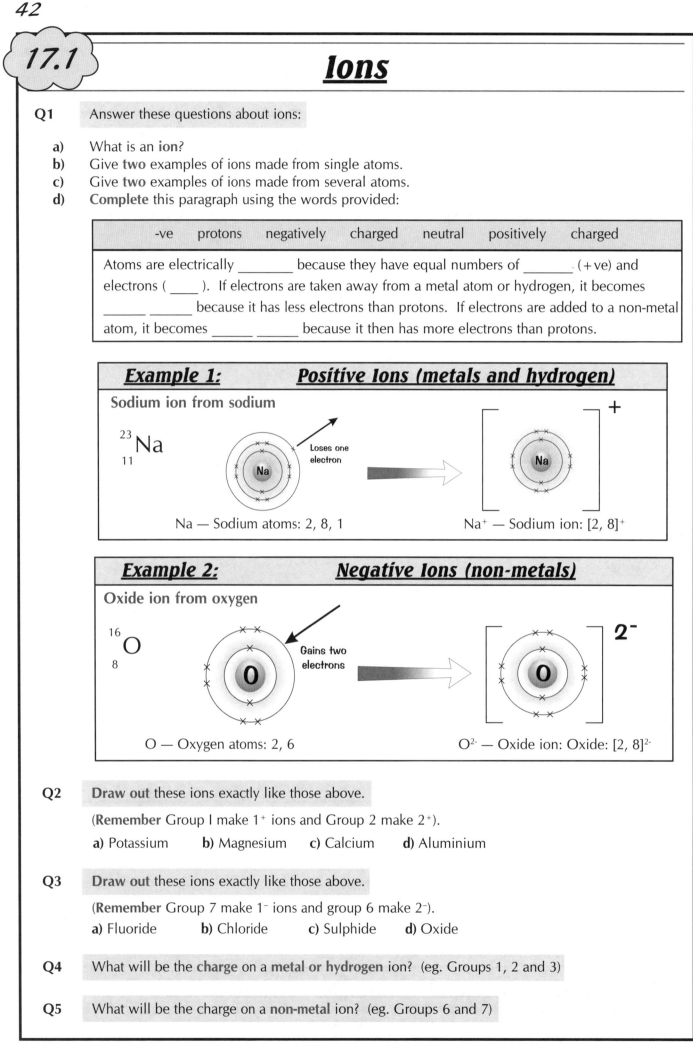

Example 1: **Positive Ions (metals and hydrogen)**

Sodium ion from sodium

$^{23}_{11}Na$ — Loses one electron

Na — Sodium atoms: 2, 8, 1   Na⁺ — Sodium ion: [2, 8]⁺

Example 2: **Negative Ions (non-metals)**

Oxide ion from oxygen

$^{16}_{8}O$ — Gains two electrons

O — Oxygen atoms: 2, 6 O^{2-} — Oxide ion: Oxide: $[2, 8]^{2-}$

Q2 **Draw out** these ions exactly like those above.

(**Remember** Group I make 1⁺ ions and Group 2 make 2⁺).
a) Potassium   b) Magnesium   c) Calcium   d) Aluminium

Q3 **Draw out** these ions exactly like those above.

(**Remember** Group 7 make 1⁻ ions and group 6 make 2⁻).
a) Fluoride   b) Chloride   c) Sulphide   d) Oxide

Q4 What will be the **charge** on a **metal or hydrogen** ion? (eg. Groups 1, 2 and 3)

Q5 What will be the charge on a **non-metal** ion? (eg. Groups 6 and 7)

Ions

Q1   Answer these questions, covering all the basics of ionic bonding:

a) What is an ionic bond?
b) If an atom gains an electron, what charge does it have?
c) If an atom loses an electron, what charge does it have?
d) Why do sodium ions have a 1^+ charge?
e) Why do chloride ions have a 1^- charge?
f) What charge would you find on a Group 2 ion?
g) What charge would you find on a Group 6 ion?
h) Why is it rare to find a 4^+ ion of carbon?

Ionic substances are tough but brittle — so don't push them too far.

Q2   **Draw** an electron configuration diagram to show what happens in the following reactions.

a) A lithium atom reacting with a chlorine atom. **Name** the compound formed.
b) A magnesium atom reacting with two chlorine atoms.

Q3   Why is sodium chloride neutrally charged?

Q4   **Draw** a picture to show the positions of sodium and chloride ions in a sodium chloride crystal.

Q5   **Name** the following ions:

a) Na^+ b) Cl^- c) S^{2-} d) NO_3^- e) SO_4^{2-} f) I^- g) F^- h) K^+ i) Ca^{2+} j) Mg^{2+} k) PO_4^{3-} l) H^+ m) Ba^{2+}

Q6   Give the **formulae** for magnesium oxide, sodium fluoride, sodium oxide, magnesium sulphate and sodium sulphate. Use the ions in the last question to help you.

Q7   Select the right answer for **a)** — **f)** from the list below:

SO_4^{2-} Mg^{2+} Kr   MgO CO_2

a) An example of a gas consisting of **single atoms**.   d) An example of a **compound**.
b) An example of a substance made from **ions**.   e) An example of an **ion**.
c) An example of a substance made from **molecules**. f) An example of a **molecular ion** (compound ion).

Q8   Which of the following properties do ionically bonded compounds have?

a) High boiling point.
b) Usually dissolve in water.
c) Conductor when solid.
d) Non-conductor when melted.
e) Weak forces hold molecules together.
f) Non-crystalline.

Top-tips: Ionic compounds are formed when electrons are <u>swapped</u> between one atom and another. They contain a metal and a non-metal — don't forget which ions are positive and which are negative.

17.2 Structures

Q1 Using the words below, **complete the table** to summarise
the properties of different types of structure:

High   Low   Poor   Good

Bonding	Structure	Melting point	Boiling point	Conductivity		
				Solid	Liquid	Aqueous solution
Ionic	Giant					
Covalent	Giant					
Covalent	Molecular					
Metallic	Giant					Not applicable

Q2 "Substances have physical properties because of their chemical properties".

Explain what this means and state whether or not you agree with it.

Q3 Why do ionic substances only **conduct electricity**
when molten or when dissolved in water?

Q4 Referring to the diagram opposite,
explain why ionic crystals dissolve in water.

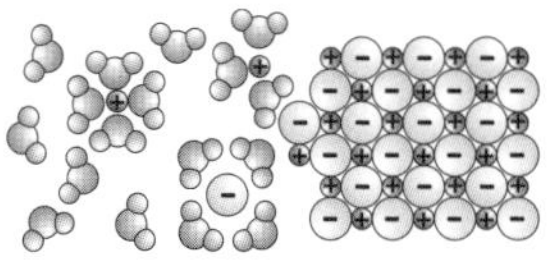

Q5 **Describe** how an atom of iron joins up to other atoms in an iron bar.

Q6 Metals have "giant structures of atoms". What is a **giant structure**?

Q7 What are "**free electrons**", and where do they originate?

Q8 How do a metal's free electrons affect its **properties**?

Q9 Answer these questions about substances changing state:

a) What is supplied to particles when you heat them?

b) What do the particles of a solid do when supplied with energy?

c) Describe how a solid melts.

d) What does the melting point of a solid mean?

e) What do the particles of a liquid do when supplied with energy?

f) What happens to water particles when it boils?

The Periodic Table

The Periodic Table is great — learn to love it.

Q1 The Periodic Table is very useful. How much do you know about it?

a) In the Periodic Table, what is meant by a **Group**?

b) In the Periodic Table, what is meant by a **Period**?

c) Roughly **how many** elements are there?

d) In what **order** are the elements listed?

e) What might be **similar** about members of the same group?

f) What might be **similar** about members of the same period?

g) Whose **idea** was it to put the elements in this order?

h) If an element is in Group I then **how many** electrons will it have in its outer electron shell?

i) If an ion has a 2⁺ charge, **which group** is it most likely to be in?

j) If an ion has a 1⁻ charge, **which group** is it most likely to be in?

Q2 In this Periodic Table, some elements are shown as letters. They're **not** the correct symbols for the elements. Use the letters to answer the questions.

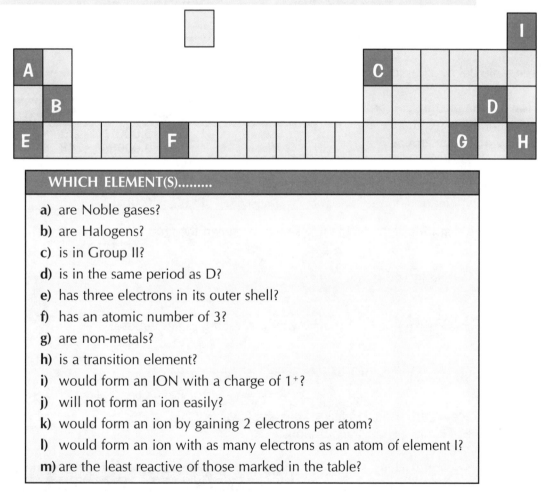

WHICH ELEMENT(S)........

a) are Noble gases?

b) are Halogens?

c) is in Group II?

d) is in the same period as D?

e) has three electrons in its outer shell?

f) has an atomic number of 3?

g) are non-metals?

h) is a transition element?

i) would form an ION with a charge of 1⁺?

j) will not form an ion easily?

k) would form an ion by gaining 2 electrons per atom?

l) would form an ion with as many electrons as an atom of element I?

m) are the least reactive of those marked in the table?

Q3 **Copy and complete** this table by filling in the **electronic configurations** of the elements:

Period	Group 1		Group 2	Group 3	Group 7	Group 0	
2	Li	2,1	Be	B	F	Ne	
3	Na		Mg	Al	Cl	Ar	2,8,8

17.3 Group 0 — The Noble Gases

The Noble Gases think they're above all this reacting business. They're so smug about having a full outer shell, they just sit around all day like they're royalty...

Q1 Here's a few easy ones to start you off...

a) **Why** are the Noble gases known as group VIII?

b) The Noble gases are "inert". **What** does this mean?

c) **Complete** the paragraph below using the word list.
Words can be used once, more than once, or not at all.

Periodic	inert	1%	diatomic	Noble	increase	low	helium
individual	argon	neon	electrons	radon	radioactive	0	

The _____ gases are found in Group_____ on the _____ Table.
The Noble gases don't react with any other element, for this reason they are also called
the _____ gases. The Noble gases have very _____ boiling points
which _____ down the group. The Noble gas with the largest atoms is
_____ and the one with the smallest atoms is _____. Noble gases
exist as _____ atoms rather than as _____ molecules. About _____
of the air is made up of Noble gases.

Q2 The table below gives information about the Noble gases. Use it to **answer these questions**:

a) How do the **melting and boiling points** of the gases change as you go down the group?

b) **Complete** the table by estimating the melting point and boiling point of radon.

Noble Gas	Atomic Number	Density at STP g/cm³	Melting Point °C	Boiling Point °C
Helium	2	0.00017	-272	-269
Neon	10	0.00084	-248	-246
Argon	18	0.0016	-189	-186
Krypton	36	0.0034	-157	-153
Xenon	54	0.006	-112	-107
Radon	86	0.01		

c) Why do the **densities** of the Noble gases increase down the group?

Q3 Why is neon used in **advertising signs**?

Neon is Ace!

Q4 Give a **common use** for argon and state why it is used for that purpose.

Q5 Why is helium used in **weather balloons**, rather than argon?

Q6 The table below shows some details of the Noble gases.
Have a look at it and answer the questions.

a) **Fill in the gaps** in the table.

b) **Write down** an element of Group 0 to match each of these descriptions:

i) Gives out a light when a current is passed through it.

ii) Less dense than air.

Noble Gas	Symbol	Atomic Number	Mass Number	No. of Protons	No. of Electrons	No. of Neutrons
	He		4	2		
Neon			20	10		
	Ar	18	40			
Krypton			84	36		
Xenon		54	131		54	
Radon		86	222			

Group 1 — The Alkali Metals

Q1 The table on the right shows four alkali metals and some of their physical properties.

Alkali Metal	Atomic Mass	Symbol	Boiling Point °C	Melting Point °C	Density g/cm³
Lithium	7		1342	181	0.535
Sodium	23		880	98	0.971
Potassium	39		760	63	0.862
Rubidium	85.5		688	39	1.53

a) Complete the table by filling in their **symbols**.

b) Caesium is the next alkali metal. Estimate its: **i) Boiling point ii) Melting point iii) Density**.

c) **Explain** why, as you go down Group I, the atoms get **bigger** in cross-section.

d) Which member of the group in the table is the **most dense**?

e) What must become **weaker** for the melting point to decrease down the group?

f) Over what **temperature ranges** would you expect **i)** Rubidium and **ii)** Potassium to be liquids?

Q2 **Complete** the table below, then answer the following questions:

Alkali Metal	No. of Protons	No. of Neutrons	No. of Electrons	Atomic Number	Mass Number
Lithium				3	7
Sodium	11				23
Potassium	19	20			
Rubidium				37	85
Caesium	55				133

a) **Draw** an atom of sodium showing its electron arrangement.

b) **How many** electrons has sodium in its outer shell?

c) Why does this make sodium so **reactive**?

d) What has to happen to an atom of sodium for it to achieve a **full** outer shell?

e) What is the **charge** of a sodium ion? **Explain** your answer.

f) When sodium bonds, it changes from an atom to an ion. What is meant by the term "**ion**"?

Q3 Put the metals in the box in order of reactivity, the most reactive first.

Caesium, Potassium, Lithium, Sodium, Rubidium.

Q4 Match up the alkali metal to its reaction in water:

A) Potassium
B) Sodium
C) Lithium

1) Ignites with yellow/orange flame, fizzes vigorously.
2) No flame, but fizzes.
3) Pops and ignites with a lilac flame, fizzes very vigorously.

Q5 When an alkali metal reacts with water, a gas is produced.

a) **Name** the gas that is produced. How could you test for this gas?

b) **Complete** the equations to the right.
Sodium + Water →
Lithium + Water →

c) i) **Complete** and **balance** this equation: $K_{(s)} + H_2O_{(l)} \rightarrow KOH_{(aq)} +$

ii) What do the symbols (s), (l), (aq), and (g) stand for in chemical equations?

I've got an electron — and I ain't afraid to use it...

With only <u>one</u> electron in their outer shell, these metals don't have much to lose — they're pretty reactive. The Exam's most likely to ask about <u>trends</u> in the group — make sure you know how <u>size</u>, <u>reactivity</u>, <u>density</u> and <u>melting</u> and <u>boiling points</u> vary down the group... and why.

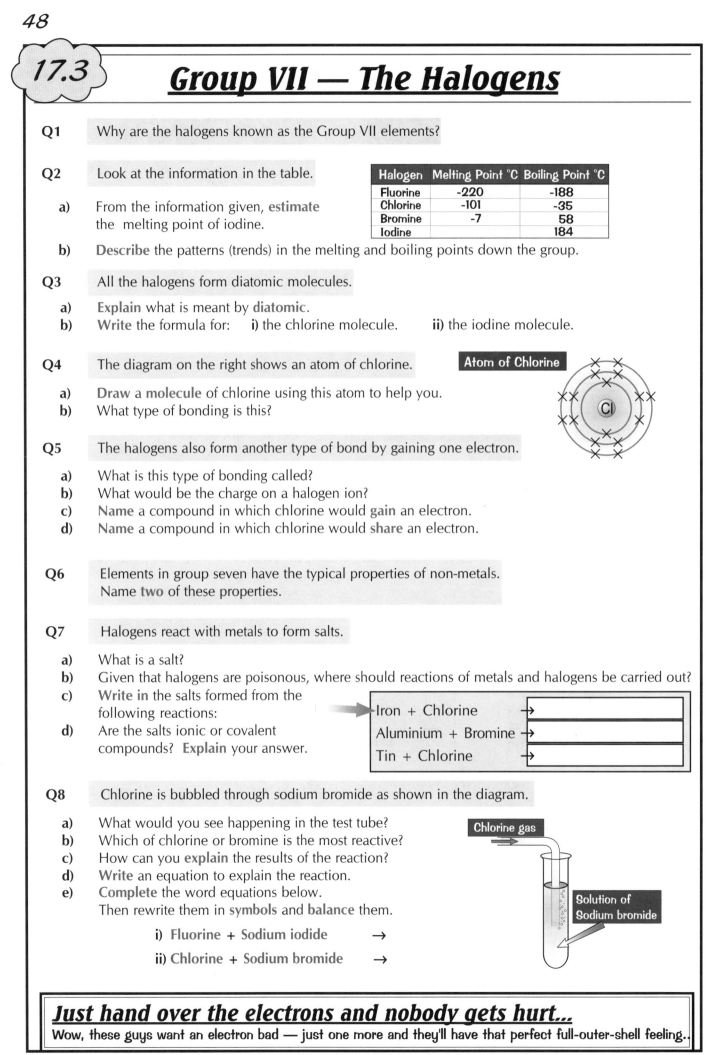

17.3

Group VII — The Halogens

Q1 Why are the halogens known as the Group VII elements?

Q2 Look at the information in the table.

Halogen	Melting Point °C	Boiling Point °C
Fluorine	-220	-188
Chlorine	-101	-35
Bromine	-7	58
Iodine		184

a) From the information given, **estimate** the melting point of iodine.

b) **Describe** the patterns (trends) in the melting and boiling points down the group.

Q3 All the halogens form diatomic molecules.

a) **Explain** what is meant by **diatomic**.
b) **Write** the formula for: **i)** the chlorine molecule. **ii)** the iodine molecule.

Q4 The diagram on the right shows an atom of chlorine.

Atom of Chlorine

a) **Draw** a **molecule** of chlorine using this atom to help you.
b) What type of bonding is this?

Q5 The halogens also form another type of bond by gaining one electron.

a) What is this type of bonding called?
b) What would be the charge on a halogen ion?
c) **Name** a compound in which chlorine would **gain** an electron.
d) **Name** a compound in which chlorine would **share** an electron.

Q6 Elements in group seven have the typical properties of non-metals. Name **two** of these properties.

Q7 Halogens react with metals to form salts.

a) What is a salt?
b) Given that halogens are poisonous, where should reactions of metals and halogens be carried out?
c) **Write in** the salts formed from the following reactions:

Iron + Chlorine →
Aluminium + Bromine →
Tin + Chlorine →

d) Are the salts ionic or covalent compounds? **Explain** your answer.

Q8 Chlorine is bubbled through sodium bromide as shown in the diagram.

a) What would you see happening in the test tube?
b) Which of chlorine or bromine is the most reactive?
c) How can you **explain** the results of the reaction?
d) **Write** an equation to explain the reaction.
e) **Complete** the word equations below. Then rewrite them in **symbols** and **balance** them.

Chlorine gas

Solution of Sodium bromide

i) Fluorine + Sodium iodide →

ii) Chlorine + Sodium bromide →

Just hand over the electrons and nobody gets hurt...

Wow, these guys want an electron bad — just one more and they'll have that perfect full-outer-shell feeling.

Electron Arrangement

Q1 Answer these atom questions:

a) An atom can be compared to the solar system. **Explain** the similarity.

b) What keeps the electrons **attracted** to the nucleus?

c) Give **another** name for an electron orbit.

Q2 **Copy and complete** the table to show the sizes of the electron shells:

Electron shell	Maximum number of electrons in the shell
1st	
2nd	
3rd	

Q3 **Copy and complete** the table below showing the properties of the first 20 elements (you'll need the Periodic Table at the front of the book).

Element	Symbol	Atomic Number	Mass Number	Number of Protons	Number of Electrons	Number of Neutrons	Electronic Configuration	Group Number
Hydrogen	H	1	1	1	1	0	1	—
Helium	He	2	4	2	2	2	2	0
Lithium	Li						2, 1	1
Beryllium								2
Boron				5				
Carbon								
Nitrogen		7						
Oxygen					8			
Fluorine							2, 7	
Neon								
Sodium		11						1
Magnesium								
Aluminium		13	27	13	13	14	2, 8, 3	3
Silicon								
Phosphorus								
Sulphur	S							
Chlorine								
Argon								
Potassium								
Calcium						20		2

Q4 Look at the table and answer these questions:

a) What is the link between **group number** and **number of outer electrons**?

b) What is the link between the **Noble gases** (group 0) and **full outer shells**?

c) Iodine is in group VII — **how many** electrons does it have in its outer electron shell?

d) Xenon is in group 0 — **how many** electrons does it have in its outer electron shell?

e) The **number of electrons** in the outer shell governs which **property** of the element?

Q5 An atom of element X has two outer electrons that do not fill the outer shell.

a) **Name** its **group**.

b) Is it a **metal** or **non-metal**?

c) Name **another** element with similar chemical properties to X.

Module Eight — Structures and Bonding

17.5 Industrial Salt

Q1 **What** is the main **use** of solid rock salt, which is especially important in the **winter months**?

Q2 Where are large quantities of **salt** found?

Q3 **How** is most of the salt obtained from the ground?

Q4 What is the **common name** for concentrated sodium chloride solution?

Q5 Sodium hydroxide has many uses. It is obtained from
rock salt industrially by electrolysis. What is **electrolysis**?

Q6 Sodium chloride is made into a solution before it is electrolysed.
Why does sodium chloride have to be made into a solution **before** electrolysis?

Q7 **Complete** the following sentences by **filling in** the missing
words (words can be used once, more than once or not at all).

brine	electrolysis	hydrogen	chlorine	rock salt
sodium	hydroxide	electrode	hydrogen	industrial
chloride	H+	atoms	negative	industrially

Sodium chloride has many _____ uses. Salt is mined as _____

_____. This is purified to give sodium chloride. Useful products are

obtained from a solution of sodium chloride called _____ by _____.

At the positive electrode _____ gas is produced. Hydrogen gas is given

off at the _____ _____. All the products from the electrolysis of brine

can be used, as _____ _____ solution is left in the reaction vessel.

Q8 Chlorine and hydrogen are formed by the electrolysis of brine. If a test
tube of each were collected, how could you **test** which contained the
chlorine and which the hydrogen (other than by looking at their colour)?

Top-tips: Learn about <u>electrolysis</u> — that's the bit you really need to know. You want to learn
the three products and exactly how they're produced. And don't forget <u>where</u> the salt comes from.

Uses of Halogens and Salt Products 17.5

Q1   Chlorine is used in bleach. Bleach is made by
dissolving chlorine in sodium hydroxide solution.

This is the reaction:

$$Cl_{2(g)} + NaOH_{(aq)} \rightarrow NaOCl_{(aq)} + NaCl_{(aq)} + H_2O_{(l)}$$

Balance the equation.

Q2   Give **two** other uses of chlorine.

Q3   Give **three** uses of sodium hydroxide.

Q4   **Fill the blanks** using the words below. Words can be used once, more than once or not at all.
(Note that some blanks may need two words in order to complete them correctly.)

sodium	hydrogencarbonate	hydrogen
chlorine	hydrocarbon	hydroxide
ammonia	paper	margarine

Brine is electrolysed to give the three products:

_____, _____ and _____.

_____ is used in making PVC, disinfecting

drinking water and in swimming pools. Hydrogen is used to

make fats such as _____.

_____ is used to make soaps and

detergents, _____ and ceramics.

Q5   Name three things that can **reduce** silver halides to silver.

Q6   What is the main **use** of silver halides?

Q7   Hydrogen halides are gases. If you **dissolved** one in water,
would you get an acidic, alkaline or neutral solution?

Sodium hydroxide — what use are you, eh?...
You've got to think of the chemical's properties — if you can see why it's good for a particular use,
it's easier to remember. Check you know what's used in bleach, margarine, soap and insecticides.

17.6 Symbols, Formulae and Equations

Q1   **Write out** the first twenty elements of the Periodic Table with their symbols.

Q2   **Write out** the symbols for the following *(without looking at the Periodic Table)*:

iron   lead   zinc   tin   copper

Q3   **Complete** this table:

Name	Formula	Proportion of each element present in substance
Zinc oxide	ZnO	1 zinc 1 oxygen
Magnesium oxide		
	NaCl	
	HCl	
Sulphur dioxide		
		1 carbon 2 oxygen
		1 sodium 1 oxygen 1 hydrogen
Potassium hydroxide		
		1 calcium 1 carbon 3 oxygen
Copper sulphate		
Potassium Hydroxide		
	H_2SO_4	
		2 Iron 3 oxygen
	$MgCl_2$	
	H_2	
		2 Chlorine

Q4   **Complete** the following:

When **chlorine** reacts with a metal to make an ionic compound, it forms a **chlor**_____.
When **oxygen** reacts with a metal to make an ionic compound, it forms an **ox**_____.
When **sulphur** reacts with a metal to make an ionic compound, it forms a **sulph**_____.

Q5   Answer the following questions about naming compounds.

a)   What name would you give to a compound made from **sodium** and **bromine**?
b)   What name would you give to a compound made from **sodium** and **flourine**?
c)   Some toothpastes contain sodium monofluorophosphate.
      What **elements** do you think are present in this compound?

Q6   **Complete** the following word equations:

a)   sodium   +   chlorine   →   _____ _____
b)   carbon   +   _____   →   carbon dioxide
c)   sulphur   +   oxygen   →   _____ _____
d)   zinc   +   oxygen   →   _____ _____
e)   _____   +   _____   →   iron sulphide
f)   potassium   +   chlorine   →   _____ _____
g)   lead   +   oxygen   →   _____ _____
h)   _____   +   _____   →   calcium oxide

Module Eight — Structures and Bonding

Equations

You won't get anywhere with chemistry without getting used to equations.
Especially symbol ones. They look horrible but you'll be fine with a little practice...

Q1 **Complete** the following **word** equations:

a) Iron	+	sulphur	→	
b) Iron	+	oxygen	→	
c) Magnesium	+	oxygen	→	
d) Sulphur	+	oxygen	→	
e) Hydrogen	+	oxygen	→	
f) Magnesium	+	sulphur	→	
g) Aluminium	+	chlorine	→	
h) Hydrogen	+	iodine	→	
i) Carbon	+	oxygen	→	

Q2 Look at the following **equation**:

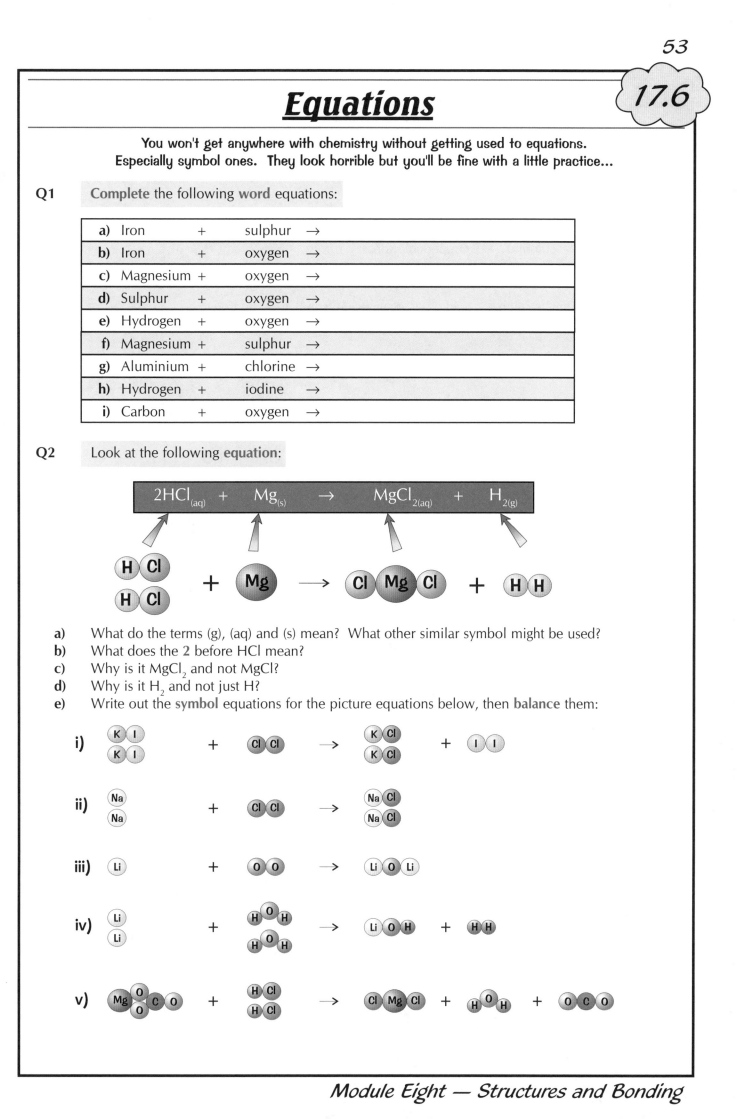

$$2HCl_{(aq)} + Mg_{(s)} \rightarrow MgCl_{2(aq)} + H_{2(g)}$$

a) What do the terms (g), (aq) and (s) mean? What other similar symbol might be used?
b) What does the **2** before HCl mean?
c) Why is it $MgCl_2$ and not MgCl?
d) Why is it H_2 and not just H?
e) Write out the **symbol** equations for the picture equations below, then **balance** them:

Module Eight — Structures and Bonding

17.6 Equations

Q1 **Write** out the **symbol** equations for these word equations:

a) Carbon + oxygen → carbon dioxide

b) Zinc + sulphuric acid → zinc sulphate + hydrogen

c) Copper + chlorine → copper chloride

d) Hydrogen + copper oxide → copper + water

e) Magnesium + sulphuric acid → magnesium sulphate + hydrogen

Q2 **Balance** the following equations by putting the correct numbers before the formulas.

a) N_2 + H_2 → NH_3

b) $CaCO_3$ + H_2SO_4 → $CaSO_4$ + H_2O + CO_2

c) H_2 + O_2 → H_2O

d) Mg + O_2 → MgO

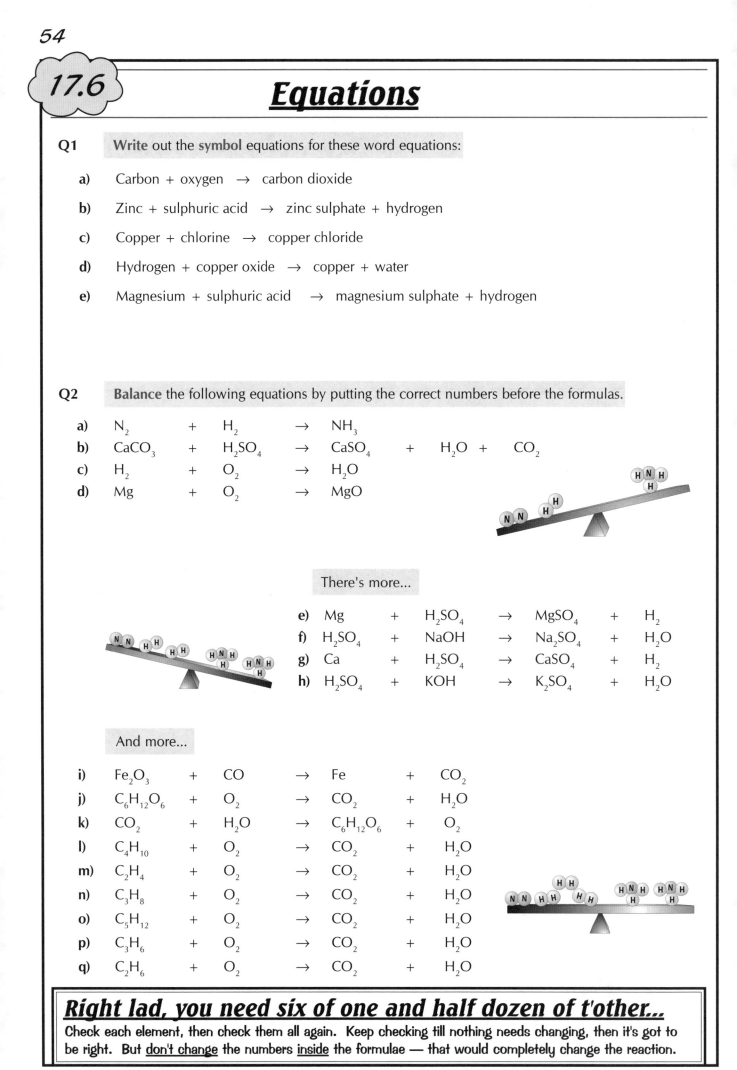

There's more...

e) Mg + H_2SO_4 → $MgSO_4$ + H_2

f) H_2SO_4 + $NaOH$ → Na_2SO_4 + H_2O

g) Ca + H_2SO_4 → $CaSO_4$ + H_2

h) H_2SO_4 + KOH → K_2SO_4 + H_2O

And more...

i) Fe_2O_3 + CO → Fe + CO_2

j) $C_6H_{12}O_6$ + O_2 → CO_2 + H_2O

k) CO_2 + H_2O → $C_6H_{12}O_6$ + O_2

l) C_4H_{10} + O_2 → CO_2 + H_2O

m) C_2H_4 + O_2 → CO_2 + H_2O

n) C_3H_8 + O_2 → CO_2 + H_2O

o) C_5H_{12} + O_2 → CO_2 + H_2O

p) C_3H_6 + O_2 → CO_2 + H_2O

q) C_2H_6 + O_2 → CO_2 + H_2O

Right lad, you need six of one and half dozen of t'other...

Check each element, then check them all again. Keep checking till nothing needs changing, then it's got to be right. But <u>don't change</u> the numbers <u>inside</u> the formulae — that would completely change the reaction.

Speed, Distance, Time

20.1

This section is based on the thinkings of Sir Isaac Newton. His ideas now allow us to work out loads of things such as how far we have gone and how fast we got there — great.

Q1   Calculate the speed of the things below in m/s:

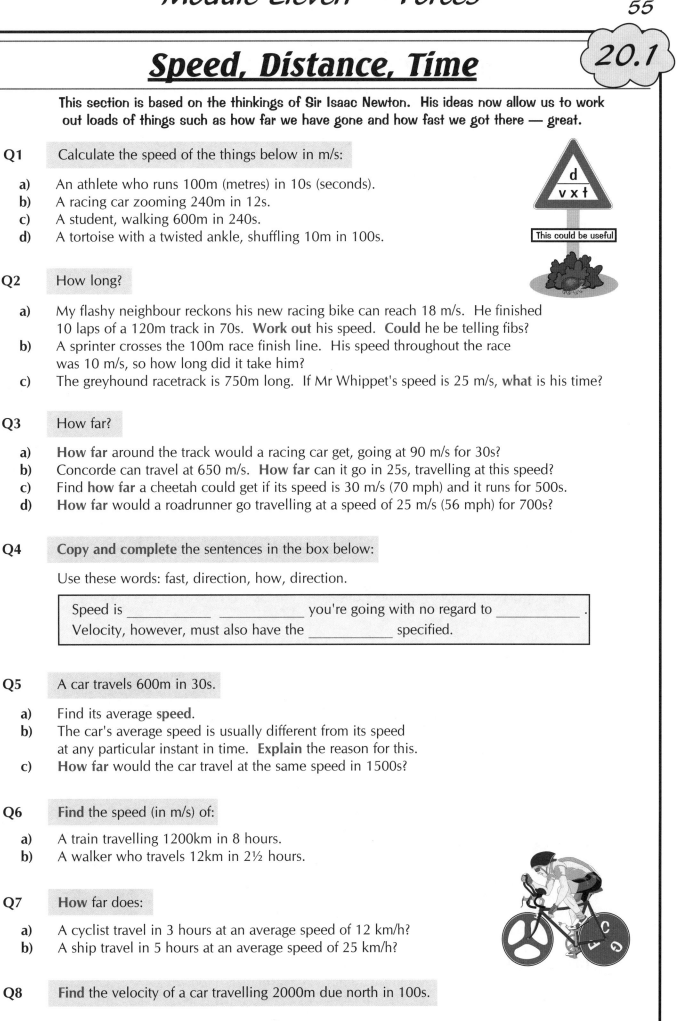

a)   An athlete who runs 100m (metres) in 10s (seconds).
b)   A racing car zooming 240m in 12s.
c)   A student, walking 600m in 240s.
d)   A tortoise with a twisted ankle, shuffling 10m in 100s.

This could be useful

Q2   How long?

a)   My flashy neighbour reckons his new racing bike can reach 18 m/s. He finished 10 laps of a 120m track in 70s. **Work out** his speed. **Could** he be telling fibs?
b)   A sprinter crosses the 100m race finish line. His speed throughout the race was 10 m/s, so how long did it take him?
c)   The greyhound racetrack is 750m long. If Mr Whippet's speed is 25 m/s, **what** is his time?

Q3   How far?

a)   **How far** around the track would a racing car get, going at 90 m/s for 30s?
b)   Concorde can travel at 650 m/s. **How far** can it go in 25s, travelling at this speed?
c)   Find **how far** a cheetah could get if its speed is 30 m/s (70 mph) and it runs for 500s.
d)   **How far** would a roadrunner go travelling at a speed of 25 m/s (56 mph) for 700s?

Q4   **Copy and complete** the sentences in the box below:

Use these words: fast, direction, how, direction.

Speed is _____ _____ you're going with no regard to _____ .
Velocity, however, must also have the _____ specified.

Q5   A car travels 600m in 30s.

a)   Find its average **speed**.
b)   The car's average speed is usually different from its speed at any particular instant in time. **Explain** the reason for this.
c)   **How far** would the car travel at the same speed in 1500s?

Q6   **Find** the speed (in m/s) of:

a)   A train travelling 1200km in 8 hours.
b)   A walker who travels 12km in 2½ hours.

Q7   **How** far does:

a)   A cyclist travel in 3 hours at an average speed of 12 km/h?
b)   A ship travel in 5 hours at an average speed of 25 km/h?

Q8   **Find** the velocity of a car travelling 2000m due north in 100s.

20.1 Speed, Velocity and Acceleration

Q1   **How long** does it take:

    a)   A car to cover 560km at an average speed of 70 km/h? *(Answer in hours.)*
    b)   Light to travel from the Sun to the Earth (150,000,000 km) at a speed of
           300,000 km/s? (Answer in minutes and seconds).

Q2   Find the velocity of a walker travelling a distance of 1000m east in 500s.

Q3   Find the velocity of a bird flying 450m south-east in 5s.

Q4   A walker starts in Barchester at 10am. She walks 5km north-east to Histon, getting there
        at 11am. She takes a half-hour break, then walks back to Barchester in 50 minutes.

    a)   What is her **velocity** (in m/s) when walking to Histon?
    b)   What is her **velocity** when walking back to Barchester?
    c)   What is her **average speed** for the whole trip?

Q5   Here's a really useful equation in a fantastic grey box:

    a)   From the equation, state what **a**, ΔV and Δt stand for.
    b)   State the usual **units** of a, ΔV and Δt.
    c)   **Explain** how acceleration is different from speed and velocity.

$$a = \frac{\Delta V}{\Delta t}$$

Q6   **Complete these sentences** using words from the list below. Use each word once only.

    acceleration   second   3 m/s   second   acceleration   4 m/s   velocity   velocity

    a)   A motorbike has a steady _____ of 3 m/s². This means that
        every _____ its _____ changes by _____.

    b)   A car has a steady _____ of 4 m/s². This means that every
        _____ its _____ changes by _____.

Q7   PC Bacon is cruising along in his car at 15 m/s.

    a)   He keeps on going for an hour. **How far** does he go, in kilometres?
    b)   A car shoots past at 80 mph. How fast is the car going
        in **kilometres per hour**, and in **metres per second**?
        (Use 1 mile = 1.6 km.)
    c)   PC Bacon gives chase, and accelerates steadily at 1 m/s² up to 40 m/s.
        How long does this take?
    d)   After travelling along for 3 minutes at 40 m/s, he catches up with the speeding car.
        How far has he travelled since reaching 40 m/s?
    e)   The speeding car is now travelling at 28 m/s. PC Bacon flags it down,
        and it pulls over into a layby. The car takes 15 s to halt. **What** is its deceleration?

Describing Motion Graphically

Q1   This velocity/time graph shows the motion of a car.

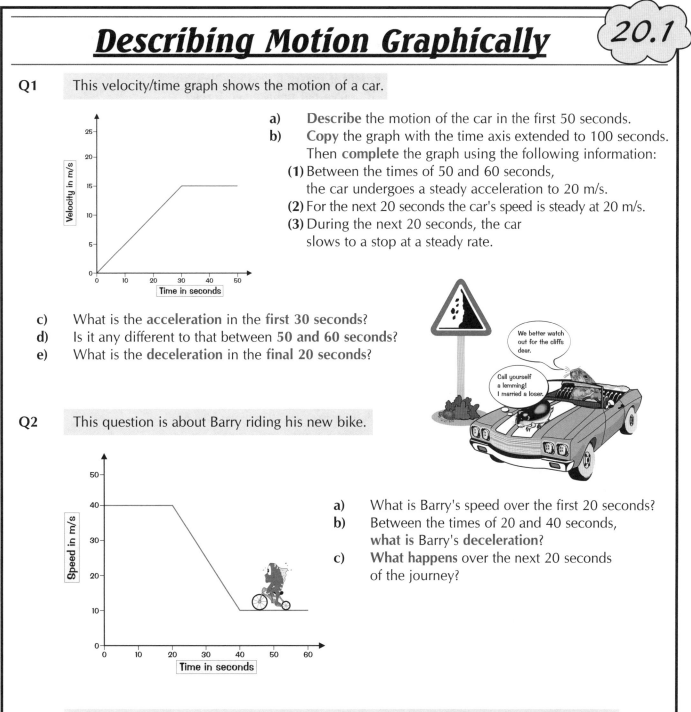

a)   **Describe** the motion of the car in the first 50 seconds.

b)   **Copy** the graph with the time axis extended to 100 seconds.
Then **complete** the graph using the following information:
(1) Between the times of 50 and 60 seconds,
the car undergoes a steady acceleration to 20 m/s.
(2) For the next 20 seconds the car's speed is steady at 20 m/s.
(3) During the next 20 seconds, the car
slows to a stop at a steady rate.

c)   What is the **acceleration** in the **first 30 seconds**?

d)   Is it any different to that between **50 and 60 seconds**?

e)   What is the **deceleration** in the **final 20 seconds**?

We better watch
out for the cliffs
dear.

Call yourself
a lemming!
I married a loser.

Q2   This question is about Barry riding his new bike.

a)   What is Barry's speed over the first 20 seconds?

b)   Between the times of 20 and 40 seconds,
what is Barry's **deceleration**?

c)   **What happens** over the next 20 seconds
of the journey?

Q3   **Draw** a distance/time graph using these measurements taken during a bike journey.
(You can assume that the bike does not go any further away than 100m before returning.)

Distance (m)	Time (s)
0	0
20	5
40	10
60	15
80	20
100	25
100	30
50	35
0	40

a) **Describe** the motion of the bike for
the whole journey by **writing labels**
on the graph.

b) **Calculate** the speed of the bike
between 20 and 25 seconds.

c) **For how long** is the bike stationary?

d) **Calculate** the speed of the bike
between 30 and 40 seconds.

e) What is the **total distance** covered
by the cyclist?

Module Eleven — Forces

Speeding Up or Slowing Down

Acceleration — very important if you're a wannabe boy-racer.
But it'll only happen if you've got <u>unbalanced</u> forces.

Q1 Fill in the **gaps** using the words below. Use each word **once** only.

bodies, large, attraction, weak, strong, field, centre, newtons, weight

Gravity is the force of _____ between _____. Between
objects on Earth, it is a _____ force, but if the mass is very very
_____ as with a planet or a star, the force of gravity can be very
_____. The region where a gravitational force can be felt is
often referred to as a gravitational _____.
The Earth's gravitational field attracts every object on Earth. This gives an
object a _____. Weight is measured in _____,
and always acts towards the _____ of the Earth.

Q2 "Mass" and "weight" are used in everyday language almost as if they were the same thing.

Draw a table with 2 columns, one headed "**mass**" and the other "**weight**".
Decide which information belongs to which column, and write them in:

- amount of matter
- measured in newtons
- measured by a balance
- not a force
- measured by a spring balance
- is a force
- caused by the pull of gravity
- same anywhere in the Universe
- measured in kilograms
- is lower on the Moon than on Earth

Q3 Be careful how you use the words weight and mass.

a) "A bag of flour weighs one kilogram".
Explain why this statement is not accurate.
b) Rewrite the above statement so that it is accurate.
c) **Copy and complete** the table opposite for a range of
masses on Earth (g = 10 N/kg).

Mass (g)	Mass (kg)	Weight (N)
5		
10		
100		
200		
500		
1000		
5000		

Q4 The strength of gravity on Earth is **g = 10 N/kg**.
Find the **weight** of rocks with the following masses:

a) 5kg   **b)** 10kg   **c)** 2.5kg

Find the **mass** of rocks with the following weights on Earth:

d) 30N   **e)** 150N   **f)** 450N

Q5 The strength of gravity on the Moon is **g = 1.6 N/kg**. Find the **weight**
of lumps of green cheese on the Moon with the following masses:

a) 5kg   **b)** 10kg   **c)** 2.5kg

Find the **mass** of rocks with the following weights on the Moon:

d) 16N   **e)** 80N   **f)** 960N

If Freda had known about the
Moon's low gravity, she never would
have entered the high jump contest.

Module Eleven — Forces

Speeding Up or Slowing Down

Q1 Use the list on the right to identify forces **a)** to **f)**.

> **a)** Acts straight downwards.   TENSION
> **b)** Slows things down.   GRAVITY or WEIGHT
> **c)** In a rope or cable.   THRUST or PUSH or PULL
> **d)** Speeds something up.   DRAG or AIR RESISTANCE or FRICTION

Q2 This question concerns a stationary object — a mug of tea — mmm, nice.

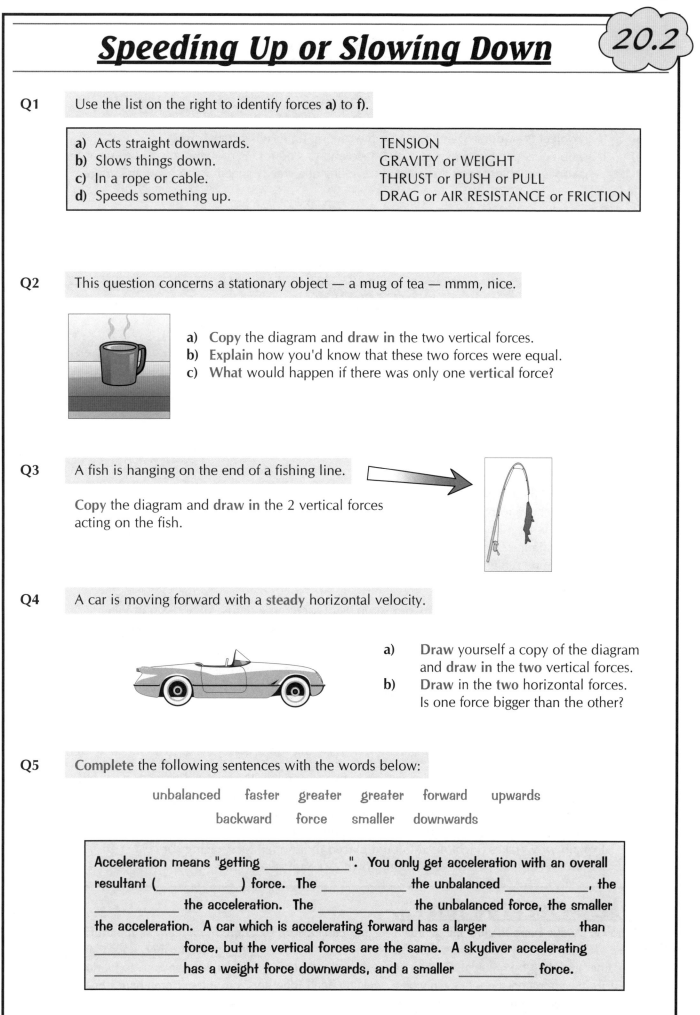

> **a)** **Copy** the diagram and **draw in** the two vertical forces.
> **b)** **Explain** how you'd know that these two forces were equal.
> **c)** **What** would happen if there was only one **vertical** force?

Q3 A fish is hanging on the end of a fishing line.

Copy the diagram and **draw in** the 2 vertical forces
acting on the fish.

Q4 A car is moving forward with a **steady** horizontal velocity.

> **a)** **Draw** yourself a copy of the diagram
>   and **draw in** the **two** vertical forces.
> **b)** **Draw** in the **two** horizontal forces.
>   Is one force bigger than the other?

Q5 **Complete** the following sentences with the words below:

>   unbalanced   faster   greater   greater   forward   upwards
>   backward   force   smaller   downwards

> Acceleration means "getting _____". You only get acceleration with an overall
> resultant (_____) force. The _____ the unbalanced _____, the
> _____ the acceleration. The _____ the unbalanced force, the smaller
> the acceleration. A car which is accelerating forward has a larger _____ than
> _____ force, but the vertical forces are the same. A skydiver accelerating
> _____ has a weight force downwards, and a smaller _____ force.

Module Eleven — Forces

20.2

Friction

Q1   Use your knowledge of **forces** acting on objects to answer the following questions.

    a)   If an object is **stationary** and has no forces acting on it, **what happens**?
    b)   If an object is moving over a rough surface and has no forces propelling it along, **what happens**?
    c)   What does an object need to continue travelling at a **steady speed** across a rough surface? **Why**?

Q2   This diagram shows how the force of friction can be measured.

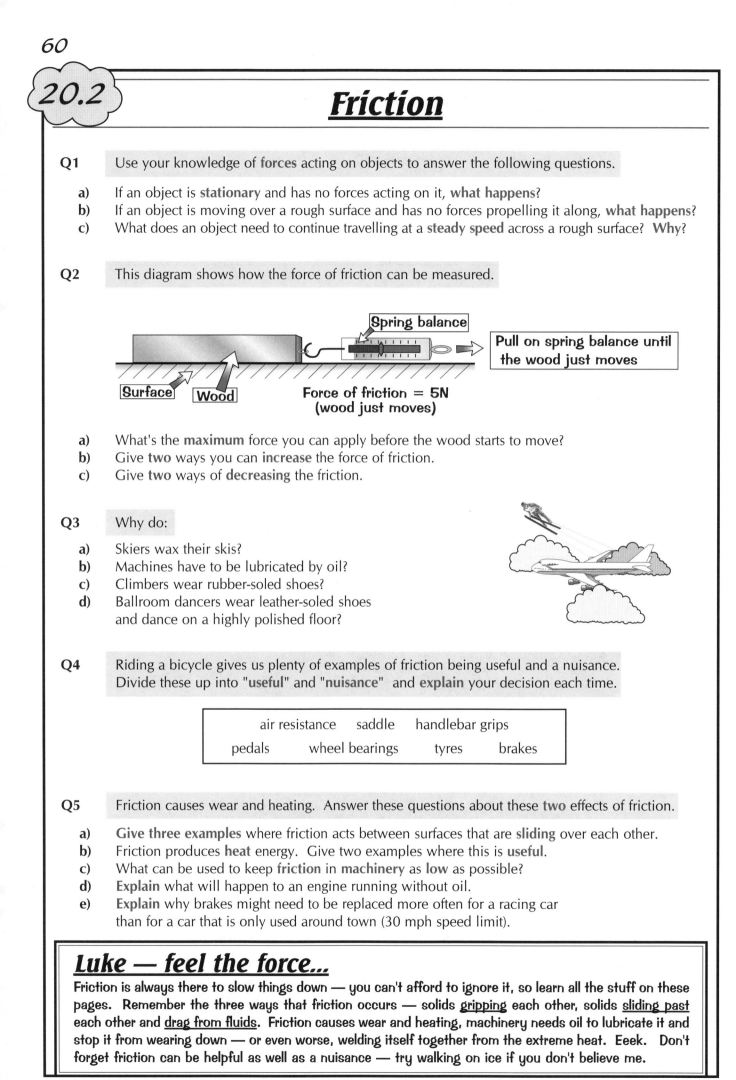

Spring balance

Pull on spring balance until the wood just moves

Surface **Wood**

Force of friction = 5N
(wood just moves)

    a)   What's the **maximum** force you can apply before the wood starts to move?
    b)   Give **two** ways you can **increase** the force of friction.
    c)   Give **two** ways of **decreasing** the friction.

Q3   Why do:

    a)   Skiers wax their skis?
    b)   Machines have to be lubricated by oil?
    c)   Climbers wear rubber-soled shoes?
    d)   Ballroom dancers wear leather-soled shoes
       and dance on a highly polished floor?

Q4   Riding a bicycle gives us plenty of examples of friction being useful and a nuisance.
    Divide these up into "**useful**" and "**nuisance**" and **explain** your decision each time.

air resistance	saddle	handlebar grips
pedals	wheel bearings	tyres	brakes

Q5   Friction causes wear and heating. Answer these questions about these **two** effects of friction.

    a)   **Give three examples** where friction acts between surfaces that are **sliding** over each other.
    b)   Friction produces **heat** energy. Give two examples where this is **useful**.
    c)   What can be used to keep **friction** in **machinery** as **low** as possible?
    d)   **Explain** what will happen to an engine running without oil.
    e)   **Explain** why brakes might need to be replaced more often for a racing car
       than for a car that is only used around town (30 mph speed limit).

Luke — feel the force...

Friction is always there to slow things down — you can't afford to ignore it, so learn all the stuff on these pages. Remember the three ways that friction occurs — solids <u>gripping</u> each other, solids <u>sliding past</u> each other and <u>drag from fluids</u>. Friction causes wear and heating, machinery needs oil to lubricate it and stop it from wearing down — or even worse, welding itself together from the extreme heat. Eeek. Don't forget friction can be helpful as well as a nuisance — try walking on ice if you don't believe me.

Force, Mass and Acceleration

Q1   Isaac Newton's First Law of Motion states that "**balanced forces**" cause no change in "**velocity**".

a)   **Explain clearly** what "balanced forces" and "velocity" mean.
b)   **Draw a diagram** of a toy train moving at a constant velocity.
     Draw in the horizontal forces.
c)   **Describe** what is meant by the term "resultant" force.
d)   For your diagram in **b) what** is the resultant force?

Q2   Newton's Second Law of Motion states that a **non-zero resultant force** causes **acceleration**.

Complete the following sentences about this law, using the words in the box below.

> force   unequal   slowing down   speeding up   stopping
> accelerate   decelerate   direction   starting

If there is an unbalanced _____, then an object will _____ or _____ in that _____.

This change in motion can take five different forms: _____, _____, _____ _____,

_____ _____ and changing direction. On a force diagram, the arrows will be _____.

Q3   What is another name given to:

a)   The downward force acting on falling bodies?
b)   Air resistance?
c)   The maximum velocity reached by a falling object?

Q4   **Plot the graph** of velocity (in m/s, on the vertical axis) against time (in s, horizontal axis) for the data in the table on the right. It shows the motion of a human skydiver after jumping out of an aeroplane. Then answer the questions **below**:

Velocity (m/s)	Time (s)
0	0
4.5	2
16.5	4
23.0	6
29.0	8
36.0	10
43.5	12
50.0	14
56.0	16
60.0	18
60.0	20

a)   **Find** the terminal velocity of the skydiver. *(Make sure you give the units)*.
b)   **Estimate** the velocity of the skydiver after:
     i) 5s   **ii)** 12.5s
c)   At what time does the skydiver reach terminal velocity?
d)   The skydiver opens her parachute 20s after jumping out of the aeroplane. Describe the extra force acting on her and its effect upon her speed.
e)   Will the skydiver reach a new terminal velocity? Explain your answer.

Q5   **Draw** the diagrams below showing the **resultant** forces. If the body is accelerating, write down the direction (up, down, right or left) in which it is accelerating.

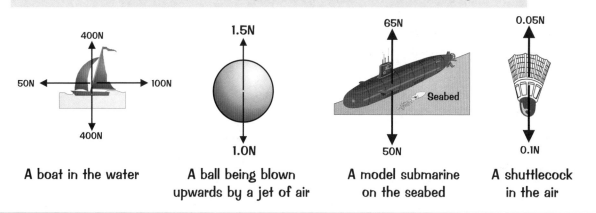

| A boat in the water | A ball being blown upwards by a jet of air | A model submarine on the seabed | A shuttlecock in the air |

20.3

Energy

The energy used or work done can be calculated using the size of the force exerted and the distance over which it acts. Don't exert yourself too much on this page.

Q1   The table below shows how the force exerted by a sprinter changes with the type of training shoe worn. It also shows the distance moved by the sprinter in a time of 2 seconds.

Brand of trainer	Force (N)	Distance (m)	Work Done
Two Stripes	4.2	1.6	
Big Cross	5.6	0.8	
Off Balance	4.8	1.2	
Obverse	5.9	1.4	
High Vest	4.5	0.9	

   a)   **Copy** the table and complete the final column showing the work done.

   b)   What **units** should be used for the work done column?

   c)   What **force** is the work mainly done against?

Q2   My old car breaks down. Luckily the road is flat. There is a garage 1500 metres away. From the car manual, I've worked out it needs a minimum force of 700N to push the car along a flat road.

   a)   What is the **minimum energy** I will need to give the car to get it to the garage?

   The car goes over a broken bottle, still 600m from the garage.
   A tyre bursts and the force of friction increases the required pushing force to 900N.

   b)   Calculate the **total energy consumption** in this case.

   Someone mentions that there is another garage only 1300m away from where my car broke down, but the last 100m are uphill, and the pushing force here would have had to be 1150N.

   c)   Would I have saved any energy by pushing the car to this garage assuming that, in both cases, I had avoided any broken bottles?

Q3   Scott and Sheila are waterskiing over a 400m course. When it's Scott's turn, a forcemeter on the tow rope registers a force of 475N. When Sheila has a go, the forcemeter registers 425N.

   a)   Calculate the **energy** needed to pull each skier over the course.

   b)   Why would the **total energy** consumed by the boat be **more** than this in each case?

   Scott now starts to show off by giving piggyback rides to passing sharks. He does this 4 times, each for 30m. For the remainder of the 400m course, he is by himself. During each piggyback, the forcemeter measures 720N.

   c)   Calculate the **energy** needed to pull Scott and his fishy friends over the course in this case.

Like the tortoise — slow and steady wins the race...
The slower something is moving, the lower its kinetic energy. Also the lighter something is, the lower its kinetic energy too. Make sure to remember work done = force × distance. Learn that and you're sorted.

Orbits

Objects are attracted to each other by a gravitational force. Between you and me this force
is tiny but between planets and satellites the force is strong enough to keep them in orbit.

Q1   Read these statements about our solar system.

For each statement, say whether it is **true or false**, and give a **reason** for your decision.

a)   All the planets are visible because of light they produce themselves.
b)   The planets in the solar system orbit around a massive object.
c)   All planets have spherical orbits.

Q2   Like all members of the Solar System, comets orbit around the Sun.

a)   Draw a diagram showing the **shape of the orbit** followed by a comet around the Sun.
b)   Name the **shape** of the **orbit** followed by a comet.
c)   **Explain how** this shape differs from the paths followed by the planets.

Q3   NASA has spent a lot of money putting the Hubble telescope into space.

a)   What are the advantages of having a telescope in space?
b)   Why is this helpful to astronomers?

Q4   The planet Jupiter has four large moons. Information about them is given in the table.

a)   Which moon is the largest?
b)   Which moon takes the longest time
     to orbit Jupiter?
c)   Europa and Io are of similar sizes. Why does
     Europa take more time to complete one orbit?
d)   As described above, four moons orbit Jupiter.
     Why doesn't Jupiter orbit its moons?

Name of Moon	Diameter (km)	Time to Orbit Jupiter (Earth Days)
Europa	3126	3.5
Callisto	4820	16.7
Io	3632	1.8
Ganymede	5276	7.2

Q5   If a space shuttle is in orbit, more than one Earth-based station is needed to communicate with it.

Why would **one station** be no good?

Q6   Artificial satellites today play an important role in our lives.
         The following statements can describe the motion of satellites.

A - a high orbit	B - in a polar orbit	C - move across the sky
D - a low orbit	E - in an equatorial orbit	F - above the atmosphere
G - orbits in a few hours	H - orbits in 24 hours	

Which of the statements above will apply to:

a)   Communications satellites?   c)   Spy satellites?
b)   Most weather satellites?   d)   Satellites broadcasting TV pictures?

Q7   Work out which of these statements are true and which are false. If it's wrong, rewrite it correctly.

a)   The Earth, the Sun, the Moon and all other bodies attract each other with a force called gravity.
b)   As the distance between two bodies increases, the force due to gravity between them increases
     more than in proportion to the increase in distance.
c)   The nearer an orbiting body is, the longer it takes to make a complete orbit.

Module Eleven — Forces

The Universe and The Stars

Milky Way — small and chocolatey. <u>The</u> Milky Way — bigger (but still tiny compared to the Universe), tastes a bit like chicken, so I'm told.

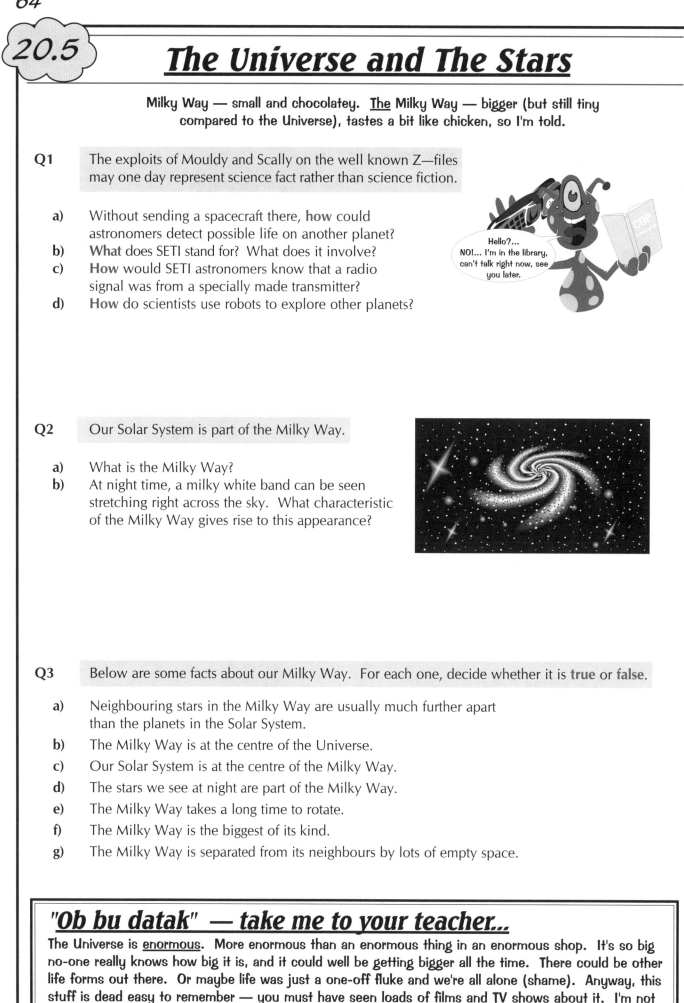

Q1 The exploits of Mouldy and Scally on the well known Z—files may one day represent science fact rather than science fiction.

a) Without sending a spacecraft there, **how** could astronomers detect possible life on another planet?

b) **What** does SETI stand for? What does it involve?

c) **How** would SETI astronomers know that a radio signal was from a specially made transmitter?

d) **How** do scientists use robots to explore other planets?

Hello?...
NO!... I'm in the library, can't talk right now, see you later.

Q2 Our Solar System is part of the Milky Way.

a) What is the Milky Way?

b) At night time, a milky white band can be seen stretching right across the sky. What characteristic of the Milky Way gives rise to this appearance?

Q3 Below are some facts about our Milky Way. For each one, decide whether it is **true** or **false**.

a) Neighbouring stars in the Milky Way are usually much further apart than the planets in the Solar System.

b) The Milky Way is at the centre of the Universe.

c) Our Solar System is at the centre of the Milky Way.

d) The stars we see at night are part of the Milky Way.

e) The Milky Way takes a long time to rotate.

f) The Milky Way is the biggest of its kind.

g) The Milky Way is separated from its neighbours by lots of empty space.

"Ob bu datak" — take me to your teacher...

The Universe is <u>enormous</u>. More enormous than an enormous thing in an enormous shop. It's so big no-one really knows how big it is, and it could well be getting bigger all the time. There could be other life forms out there. Or maybe life was just a one-off fluke and we're all alone (shame). Anyway, this stuff is dead easy to remember — you must have seen loads of films and TV shows about it. I'm not saying you can spend all your revision time watching ET though — you've still got to learn it...

Module Eleven — Forces

The Life Cycle of Stars

Q1 Astronomers have been studying groups of stars. They've used their observations to come up with an idea for how they think some of the stars evolved.

This "**Life Cycle**" is illustrated in the diagram below.

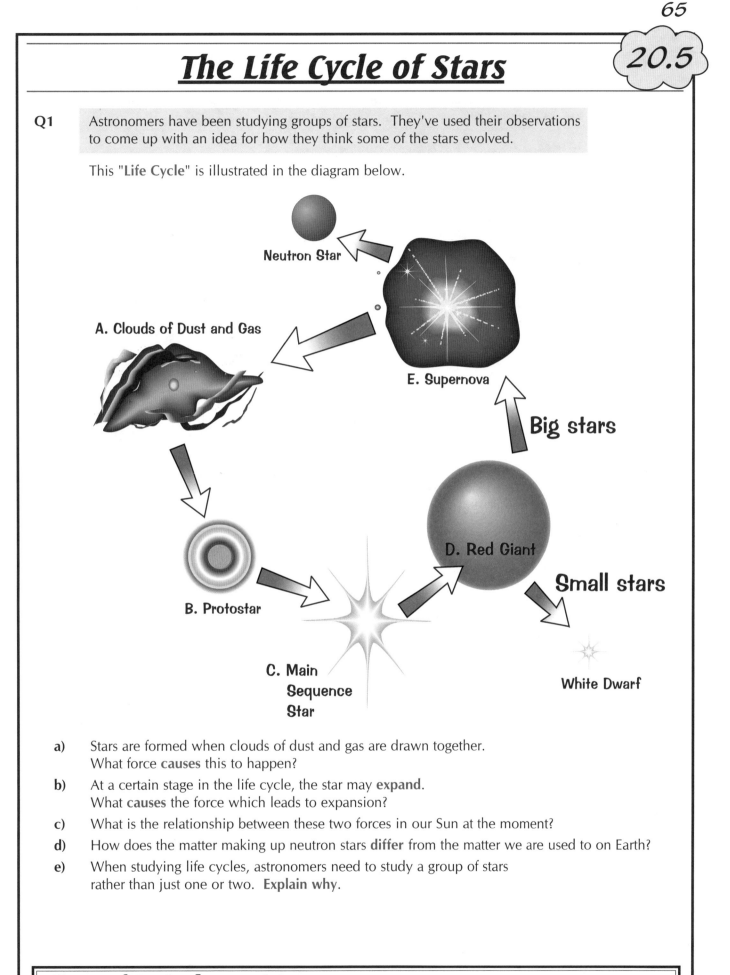

a) Stars are formed when clouds of dust and gas are drawn together.
What force **causes** this to happen?

b) At a certain stage in the life cycle, the star may **expand**.
What **causes** the force which leads to expansion?

c) What is the relationship between these two forces in our Sun at the moment?

d) How does the matter making up neutron stars **differ** from the matter we are used to on Earth?

e) When studying life cycles, astronomers need to study a group of stars
rather than just one or two. **Explain why**.

I'm going to be a star...

The lifetime of a star is quite complicated — see the diagram above. Learn it — the order, labels and pictures. Do that and you'll have no problem describing each stage.

21.1 *Waves: Basic Principles*

May there be <u>light</u> in your <u>pre-exam lives</u>, and if <u>music</u> be the <u>food of love</u> then turn your stereos off.
They'll only distract you. OK, enough of that. Do some questions.

Q1   Copy the following sentences and **fill in the gaps**.

a)   There are two different types of wave motion: _____ and _____.

b)   The number of waves per second passing a fixed point is called the _____, and is measured in _____.

c)   The time taken for two adjacent crests to pass a fixed point is called the _____, and is measured in _____.

d)   The maximum distance of particles from their resting position is called the _____.

e)   The distance travelled each second by a wave is called its _____ and is measured in _____.

f)   Waves will change their speed and wavelength when they go into different materials. This is called _____.

g)   Waves will spread out when they pass through a small gap. This is called _____.

Q2   What does a wave transfer?

Q3   You can send a wave along a piece of string by shaking one end up and down (see diagram).

a)   How would you increase the **frequency** of this wave?

b)   How would you increase its **amplitude**?

Q4   You are floating in the sea, measuring waves (as you do). You record five seconds between one crest passing and the next.

a)   What is the frequency of this wave?

b)   By watching the waves move along a breakwater you estimate that the distance between 10 crests is about 30m. Work out the average **wavelength** of the waves.

c)   **How far** have the waves travelled each time a crest passes you?

d)   **How long** does it take the wave to pass you?

e)   How far does the wave travel in **one** second?

f)   What is the **speed** of the wave?

g)   **Which way** do you move as the wave passes through you?

Q5   There are six equations below, some of which are incorrect or incomplete. Write down the correct versions, first in words, then using the usual symbols.

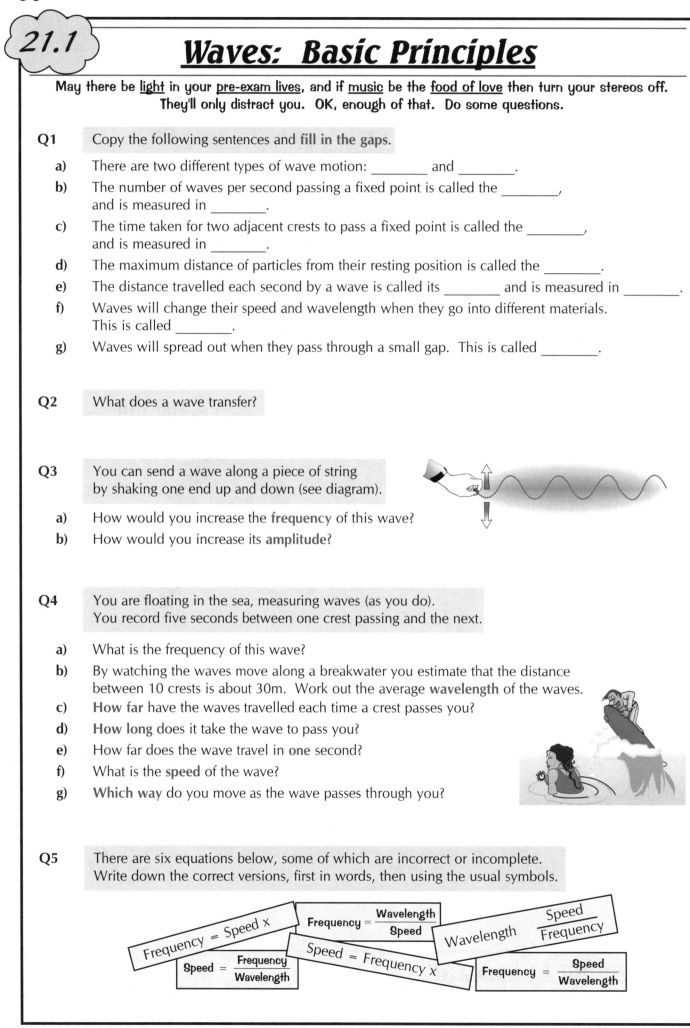

Frequency = Speed x

$$\text{Frequency} = \frac{\text{Wavelength}}{\text{Speed}}$$

$$\text{Wavelength} = \frac{\text{Speed}}{\text{Frequency}}$$

$$\text{Speed} = \frac{\text{Frequency}}{\text{Wavelength}}$$

Speed = Frequency x

$$\text{Frequency} = \frac{\text{Speed}}{\text{Wavelength}}$$

Reflection and Refraction

Q1 Light can be reflected at a surface. Complete the passage below using using the following words:

reflect   clear   shiny   dull

> Some objects give out light. We see everything else because they _____ light.
> Some objects reflect light without sending it off in many different directions.
> This is called a _____ reflection and objects which do this look _____.
> Most objects send the reflected light in many different directions, and these
> objects look _____.

Q2 What is the name for a beam of light used to represent a light path?

Q3 What is the name for the line drawn at right angles to a mirror surface?

Q4 The diagrams 1 and 2 show rays arriving at a surface.

Make a copy of each diagram and draw the reflected rays.

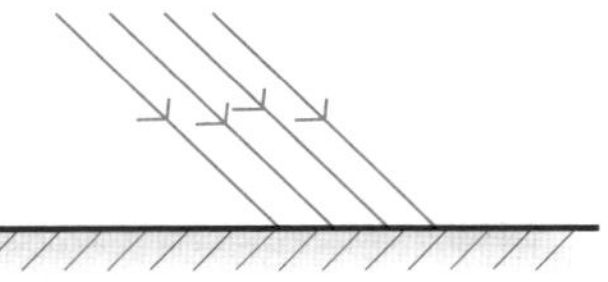

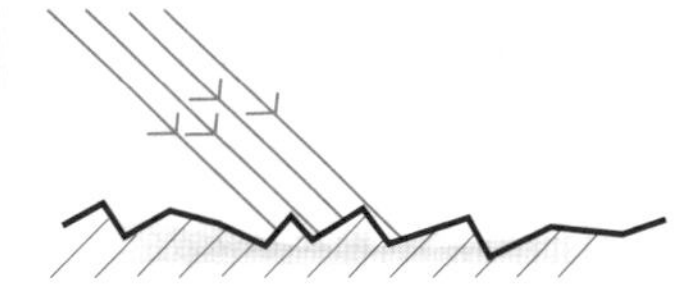

Q5 Study this plan view of two people sitting on a park bench.

They can see some statues reflected in the window.

Use the law of reflection to decide **which of the statues**, A, B, C and D, persons 1 and 2 can see.

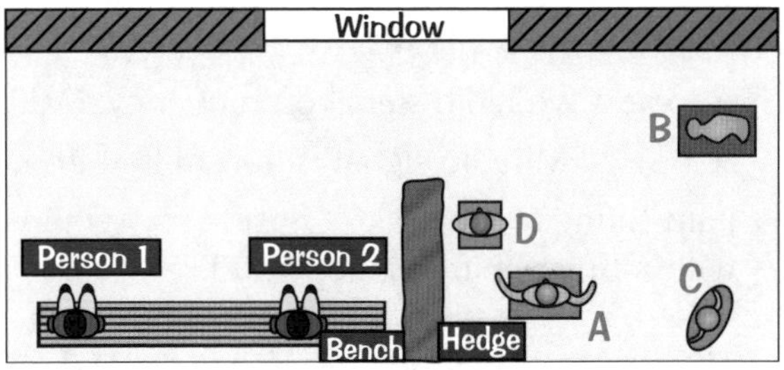

Q6 **Choose the correct words** for the following sentences about refraction.

a) Light travels at different (**speeds** / **wavelengths**) in different media.

b) The change of speed occurs at the (**surface** / **boundary**) of the two media.

Q7 What is meant by the "**normal**" to a surface?

Q8 Does the **frequency** of light change when it enters a different medium?

21.1

Diffraction

Q1 Study the rays in the two diagrams on the right.

a) In Diagram 1, a ray **enters** a glass block.
Which ray (X, Y or Z) shows how it would continue?

b) In Diagram 2, a ray **leaves** the block.
Which ray (A, B or C) shows its path correctly?

Q2 **Circle the right words** to make these sentences correct.

When a ray of light enters a glass block it is bent (**towards / away from**) the normal.
When a ray of light leaves the glass block it is bent (**towards / away from**) the normal.

Q3 **Fill in the gaps** in the following sentences.

a) Waves will _____ when they go through a _____ or past an _____ .

b) This effect is called _____ .

c) The _____ the gap, the more diffraction there is.

d) If the gap is about the same size as the _____ of the wave,
a _____ _____ shaped wave will be produced.

Q4 A sound wave and visible light wave pass through a doorway 75cm wide.

a) What **frequency of sound** has a wavelength of 75cm? Can a human **hear** this sound?

b) If the visible light wave has a frequency of 5×10^{14} Hz, what is its wavelength?

c) Use the results of your calculations from **a)** and **b)** to **explain**
why you can hear around corners, but not see around them.

(In your calculations, take the speed of sound to be 330 m/s and the speed of light to be 3×10^8 m/s.)

Q5 Would you get much diffraction in the following situations? What would be the effect?

a) A long wave radio signal of frequency 1MHz passes between two blocks of flats 250m apart.

b) A 1GHz FM radio signal is transmitted from the far side of a short tunnel that is 6m wide.

c) I am sitting at my desk. Outside my window (50cm wide) someone's serenading me
with a trumpet (frequency 5000Hz).

Q6 The diagrams below show shortwave TV waves and longwave radio waves approaching a hill.

a) Copy and complete the pictures above, showing how the hill changes the direction of the wave.

b) Suggest a reason why people in the houses in the picture can **listen** to the cricket
on long wave Radio 4 but not **watch** it on the television.

Module Twelve — Waves and Radiation

The Elecromagnetic Spectrum

Q1 Copy and complete the following paragraphs about electromagnetic waves.

a) Electromagnetic (EM) waves form a continuous_____. In any given

_____, all EM waves travel with roughly the same _____.

In a _____ this_____ is about 3 x 10⁸ m/s. There are

_____ main types of EM wave. The correct order for these types of EM

wave is (beginning with longest wavelength):

_____ _____, _____, _____, _____ _____,

_____, _____ and _____ _____.

b) _____ waves have the lowest frequency and the _____

wavelength, and _____ _____ have the highest frequency and the

_____ wavelength.

Our eyes are sensitive to EM waves from the _____ _____ spectrum only.

Q2 Decide whether each of the statements **a)** to **j)** below are **true or false.**
If false, write down what the **highlighted words** should be replaced with.

a) **Microwaves** are used to communicate with satellites.

b) **Microwaves** are the same thing as heat radiation.

c) **Gamma rays** both cause and cure cancer.

d) Only **visible light** will show diffraction.

e) **Radio waves** can have wavelengths of many metres.

f) **X-rays** are used to take pictures of bones because they are relatively safe.

g) **Infrared** radiation causes skin cancer.

h) **Microwaves** are absorbed by water.

i) **Long wave radiowaves** are able to diffract long distances round the Earth.

j) **Visible light** has a wavelength of about a ten thousandth of a millimetre.

A cold and calculating mind...

Once you've got the hang of them, 'doing' questions like calculations, and 'fill in the blank'-type things are much easier to get marks on than 'thinking' questions (the innocent-looking-but-evil 'explain why' and 'in what way' questions). Often though, a question will have several parts, with only the last one needing much thinking. Even if that bit stumps you, you should clean up on the rest. <u>Go forth and calculate!</u>

21.2 The Electromagnetic Spectrum

Q1 The diagram shows parts of the electromagnetic spectrum and wavelengths for the different radiations — but they're all mixed up.

a) **Draw** your own diagram of a spectrum, but with the types of radiation and wavelengths in the correct order, from the shortest to the longest wavelength.

b) How many times longer is a typical visible light wave compared with an X-ray wave?

c) How many times longer is a microwave compared with a typical visible light wave?

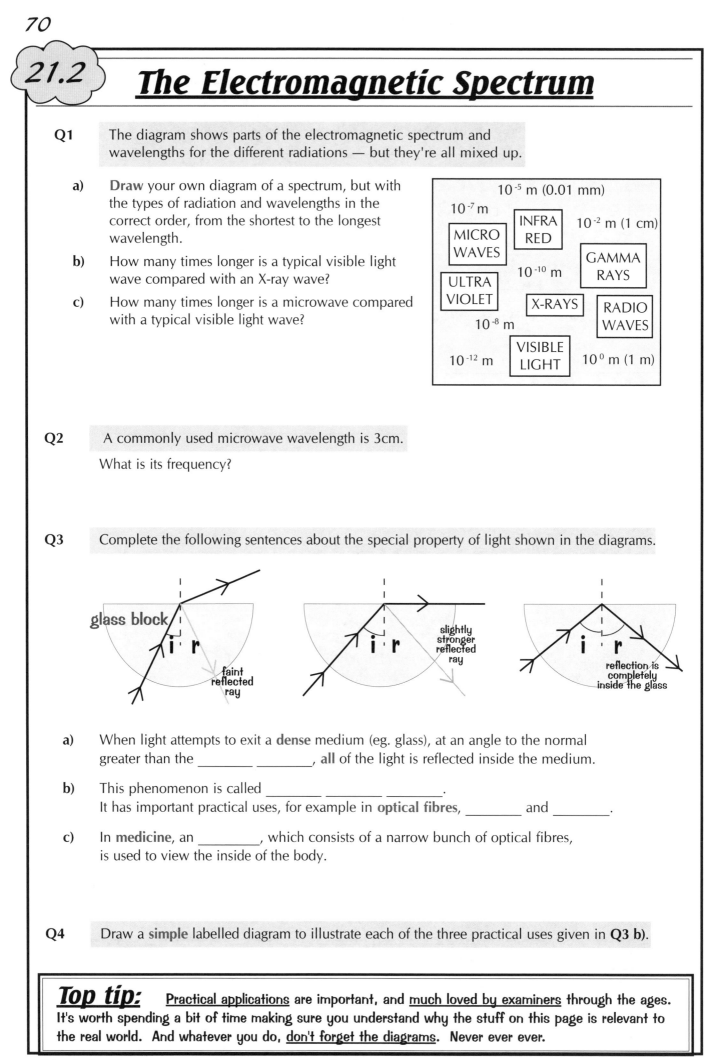

10^{-5} m (0.01 mm)
10^{-7} m
INFRA RED
10^{-2} m (1 cm)
MICRO WAVES
GAMMA RAYS
10^{-10} m
ULTRA VIOLET
X-RAYS
RADIO WAVES
10^{-8} m
10^{-12} m
VISIBLE LIGHT
10^{0} m (1 m)

Q2 A commonly used microwave wavelength is 3cm.

What is its frequency?

Q3 Complete the following sentences about the special property of light shown in the diagrams.

glass block
i r
faint reflected ray

i r
slightly stronger reflected ray

i r
reflection is completely inside the glass

a) When light attempts to exit a **dense** medium (eg. glass), at an angle to the normal greater than the _____ _____, **all** of the light is reflected inside the medium.

b) This phenomenon is called _____ _____ _____.
It has important practical uses, for example in **optical fibres**, _____ and _____.

c) In **medicine**, an _____, which consists of a narrow bunch of optical fibres, is used to view the inside of the body.

Q4 Draw a **simple** labelled diagram to illustrate each of the three practical uses given in **Q3 b)**.

> **Top tip:** Practical applications are important, and much loved by examiners through the ages. It's worth spending a bit of time making sure you understand why the stuff on this page is relevant to the real world. And whatever you do, don't forget the diagrams. Never ever ever.

Module Twelve — Waves and Radiation

The Electromagnetic Spectrum

Q1   This table is all mixed up. **Redraw** the table with the information in the **correct** places.

Type of Radiation	Effects on Living Tissue	Uses
Gamma	• probably none	• communication • broadcasting • radar
X-Ray	• heating of water in tissues can cause "burning"	• imaging internal structures in the body • studying the atomic structure of materials
UV	• kills living cells in high doses • lower doses can cause cells to become cancerous • causes tanning	• fluorescent tubes • tanning • security marking
Visible	• kills living cells in high doses • lower doses can cause cells to become cancerous • kills cancerous cells	• kill bacteria in food • sterilise medical equipment • treat tumours
IR	• kills living cells in high doses • lower doses can cause cells to become cancerous	• radiant heaters • grills • remote controls • thermal imaging
Microwave	• causes burning of tissues	• satellite communication • cooking
Radio	• activates sensitive cells in the retina	• seeing • optical fibre communication

Q2   Radiation absorption by biological tissues can have harmful consequences.

a)   When radiation is absorbed, the energy it carries can be converted into **two** forms. Name them.

b)   In general, is **low wavelength, high frequency** radiation more or less harmful than **high wavelength, low frequency** radiation?

c)   Jessica Rarebit is sunning herself. Write down **two** ways in which she can protect against electromagnetic waves in the sunlight which are likely to cause **sunburn** or **skin cancer**.

d)   Professor Lex Ray is conducting highly dodgy experiments with radioactive sources emitting gamma rays. What steps can he take to protect himself?

21.2 — The Electromagnetic Spectrum

Q1 Stephen is a **pasty-coloured** lad from Cheltenham who spends most of his summer sunbathing topless on the lawn. His friend Harshan, a **dark skinned** Sri-Lankan, spends most of his summer sniggering at Stephen.

Explain why Stephen is more at risk from skin cancer than Harshan.

Q2 Information such as speech or music can be converted into electrical signals. These signals can then be transmitted as either digital or analogue signals.

a) Write down how digital and analogue signals are **different**.

b) **List three** examples of devices which use each type of signal.

Q3 Decide whether the following statements are **true or false**. If false, write out the correct version.

a) The **amplitude** and **frequency** of **digital** signals vary continuously.

b) **Digital** pulses can take one of only **two** forms: ON or OFF.

c) Clocks, phones and dimmer switches can **all** be **analogue** devices.

d) Clocks, phones and on/off switches can **all** be **digital** devices.

e) **Digital** pulses can take one of only **two** forms: 1 or 0.

f) The problem with **digital** signals is that they lose quality over relatively short distances.

g) **Digital** signals are capable of transmitting far more information than **analogue** ones (within a given time).

h) **Analogue** signals are **turkeys** to the **sleek golden eagles** of **digital**.

i) But like turkeys, they have their uses.

Q4 Give **two** advantages of digital signals over analogue.

Q5 Why are **analogue** signals still preferred for some uses?

Pulsating stuff this...

This all follows on neatly from optical fibres and what-not, so you can bet you'll get a question on it. Make sure you know the <u>differences</u> between analogue and digital signals, and <u>why</u> digital signals are better. And 'because we can watch the footy and loads of cool movies' is not an exam answer.

Module Twelve — Waves and Radiation

Radioactive Substances

Radioactivity has provided the plot for far too many really pointless movies.
But it does have its <u>uses</u>, and examiners like <u>asking about them</u> (the uses that is, not the movies).

Q1 The diagram below shows alpha, beta and gamma radiation being fired at a line of obstacles.

a) **Copy** the diagram.
For each particle, draw a line
to **show the path** it travels
before it's absorbed.

b) Give a reason why alpha
particles only penetrate a
short distance into a material.

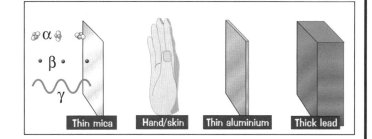

Q2 When radiation travels through matter it can cause **ionisation**.

a) Explain what is meant by the term "**ionisation**".

The diagram shows a simplified drawing of an
experiment to demonstrate that radiation
can ionise matter.
The space between the plates is filled with argon
gas at low pressure. A current is measured.

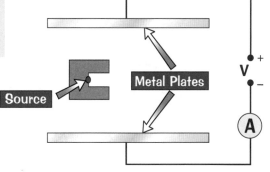

b) Name the **two different** particles formed
when radiation from the source ionises an
argon atom.

c) **Describe** how this leads to a
current in the circuit.

d) The argon gas is removed from between the plates,
leaving a vacuum behind. **Explain** why there is now no current flow.

Q3 This question concerns the treatment of cancer using radiotherapy.

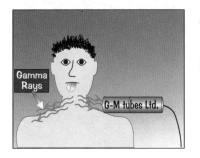

a) High doses of gamma rays can be used to treat cancers.
What effect do gamma rays have on living cells?

b) **Explain** why a patient on a course of radiotherapy
feels very ill.

21.3 *Effects of Radiation*

Q1 Radioactive particles can be harmful to living cells.

a) Which **types of radiation** can do this damage?

b) What **process** usually has to happen for damage to occur?

c) Which part of the cell controls **cell function**?

d) What is the name of a cell that has been **slightly altered**, but not killed?

e) Why are these cells so **dangerous**?

f) What is the name for the **condition** commonly caused by these cells?

Q2 Different types of radiation cause varying degrees of damage to cells.

a) Which of an **alpha particle**, a **beta particle** or a **gamma ray** is likely to cause the **most damage** to cells?

b) Why's this type of radiation more dangerous? Give **two reasons**.

Q3 List **at least three factors** which determine how much harm is done to a person when exposed to radiation.

Q4 What type(s) of radiation are most dangerous when **outside** the body?

Explain your answer.

Q5 What type(s) of radiation are most dangerous when **inside** the body?

Explain your answer.

Q6 A radiation burn can look just like a normal burn, with redness and blistering around the affected area, but will heal **a lot more slowly**. Why do you think this is?

Q7 Young children and developing embryos are particularly susceptible to the effects of radiation. Why is this?

Q8 Radioactive substances are often referred to as having a **half-life**.

a) What does this mean?

b) Using a Geiger counter, the activity of a radioactive source was measured at 800 counts/sec. Fifteen minutes later, it was down to 400 counts/sec. What is its **half-life**?

It was a long time before anyone discovered what had happened to the children in the shed that day.

c) What count rate would you expect to measure after **a full hour**?

Atomic Structure

Q1   The diagram opposite shows the particles that constitute an atom.

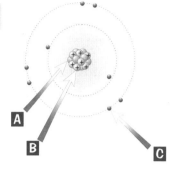

a)   **Name the particles** labelled A, B and C.

b)   What stops the electrons from flying away from the nucleus?

c)   How many **neutrons** are there in the nucleus
if there are 16 nucleons in this atom?

Q2   There are **three** different types of particle within an atom.

a)   Name them.

b)   Which **two** of these particles would you find in the **nucleus** of an atom?

c)   Where would you find the other one?

d)   Which type of particle is **electrically neutral**?

e)   Which **two** particles carry **opposite charges**?

f)   Where in the atom is most of the **mass** concentrated?

g)   Explain why this is.

Q3   **Complete the table** below which summarises the relative
mass and electrical charges of the sub-atomic particles.

Particle	Relative Mass	Electric Charge
Proton		
Neutron		
Electron		

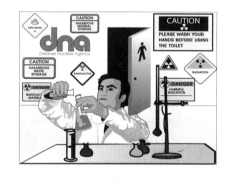

Q4   The diagram below shows the apparatus used by
Ernest Rutherford to probe the structure of the atom.

a)   **Name the particles** that are directed at the gold foil.

b)   Why does this apparatus need to operate in a **vacuum**?

c)   Which of the detectors measures the **highest** count rate?

d)   Some particles are detected at Y. **Explain** this
observation using your knowledge of atomic structure.

e)   Just a very small fraction of the incident particles
are scattered more than 90° by the foil (some of
these are detected by detector Z). What does
this tell you about the **nuclei** of the gold atoms?

f)   Gold was chosen as the target for this experiment.
Give a **reason** for this choice.

g)   Explain why a **gaseous** target would be unsuitable.

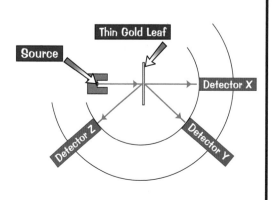

21.4

Radioactive Decay

Q1   A stable atom of bismuth has a **mass number** of 209.

  a)   Explain what is meant by "**mass number**".

       The **atomic number** of bismuth is 83.

  b)   Calculate the number of neutrons in the nucleus of a **stable** bismuth atom.

  c)   Describe how the structure of an **unstable** atom of bismuth
       will be different to a **stable** atom of bismuth.

Q2   Copy the table opposite and
       fill in the missing data.

	Number of electrons	Number of protons	Number of neutrons	Mass Number	Symbol
oxygen-16		8			$^{16}_{8}O$
aluminium-27	13				
radium-226		88			
strontium-90	38				
hydrogen-3		1			

Q3   **Copy and complete** the following paragraph about isotopes
       using the given words. You may use a word more than once:

atomic	mass	neutrons	electrons
element	energy	protons	atoms

       Isotopes of the same _____ have equal numbers of _____ and _____
       but different numbers of _____. Hence they have the same _____ number
       but a different _____ number.

Q4   Information about six atoms A, B, C, D, E and F is given below.

       | Atom A: 8 neutrons, mass number 16 | | Atom D: 6 neutrons, mass number 11 |
       | Atom B: 3 electrons, mass number 7 | | Atom E: 3 neutrons, mass number 6 |
       | Atom C: 8 protons, mass number 17 | | Atom F: 6 protons, mass number 12 |

       For which three atoms do you not need the mass number to identify the element?

Q5   **Radioactive isotopes** in certain substances (eg. rocks
       and fossils) can be used to help **date** that substance.

       Explain **briefly** how this is possible.

Q6   **Radioactive isotopes** of **uranium** are incorporated
       into igneous rock when the rock is formed.
       These naturally decay to form **stable lead** isotopes.

       What would a **low uranium to lead ratio** in a piece of
       igneous rock tell you about the age of that rock?

Module Twelve — Waves and Radiation

Sound Waves

Q1   What has to happen for a sound wave to be created?

Q2   What **vibrates** in the objects below to start a sound?

| Drum | Violin | Loudspeaker | Voice |

Q3   Are sound waves **longitudinal** or **transverse**?

Q4   Answer these questions using the six frequencies in the box below.

   a)   Which two frequencies are **identical**?

   b)   Which is closest to the lowest frequency **humans** can hear?

   2Hz,   20Hz,   200Hz,   2000Hz,   2kHz,   20kHz

   c)   For which one could you easily count the vibrations without instruments?

   d)   Which is closest to the **highest** frequency humans can hear?

Q5   Sarah is experimenting with an oscilloscope and a signal generator connected to a loudspeaker.

She draws an oscilloscope trace for a range of frequencies and amplitudes (see opposite) but gets the labels mixed up.

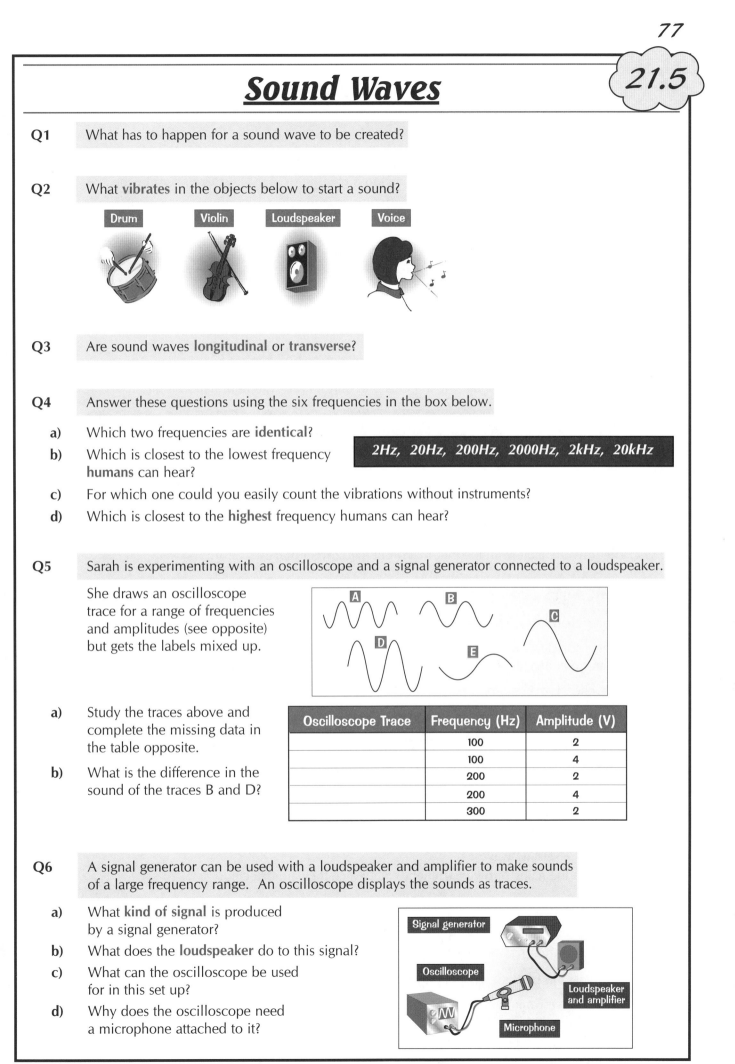

   a)   Study the traces above and complete the missing data in the table opposite.

   b)   What is the difference in the sound of the traces B and D?

Oscilloscope Trace	Frequency (Hz)	Amplitude (V)
	100	2
	100	4
	200	2
	200	4
	300	2

Q6   A signal generator can be used with a loudspeaker and amplifier to make sounds of a large frequency range. An oscilloscope displays the sounds as traces.

   a)   What **kind of signal** is produced by a signal generator?

   b)   What does the **loudspeaker** do to this signal?

   c)   What can the oscilloscope be used for in this set up?

   d)   Why does the oscilloscope need a microphone attached to it?

Module Twelve — Waves and Radiation

21.5 Ultrasound

Q1 Copy and complete the following:

"Sounds above 20 000 Hz have too high a _____ to be heard by the human ear. Sounds above this frequency are called _____."

Q2 Calculate the wavelengths of the following ultrasound frequencies in air. *(Take the speed of sound in air to be 330m/s.)*

a) 25kHz   **b)** 30kHz   **c)** 50kHz   **d)** 100kHz

Q3 You need to be able to describe several applications of ultrasound.

Below is a table summarising three uses of ultrasound. The information is all mixed up.

Application	Category of use	Ultrasound used to	Basic principles
Quality control	Industrial	Image the foetus	Use of energy in ultrasound to physically alter material
Pre-natal screening	Medical	Check for cracks in metal castings	Detection of reflected ultrasound to build image
Cleaning	Industrial	Cleaning delicate mechanisms without dismantling them	Detection of reflected ultrasound to build image

Redraw the table with the information in the **correct places**.

Q4 Why is ultrasound...

a) better than X-rays for creating an image of a foetus?

b) better for cleaning delicate mechanisms than traditional methods?

c) the chosen method for detecting flaws in metal castings?

21.6 Seismic Waves

Q1 We can learn about the interior of the Earth by measuring seismic waves.

a) What are **seismic waves**?

b) What is the **name of the instrument** with which they are detected?

Q2 The diagram opposite shows the **model** we have developed for the Earth using information gathered from seismic waves.

a) **Copy** it, and label the different layers of the Earth.

b) Why do we work out the Earth's structure from seismic wave activity rather than drill into it to take measurements?